50 THINGS TO SEE ON THE MOON

A FIRST-TIME STARGAZER'S GUIDE

John A. Read

With foreword by David M. F. Chapman

Stellar Publishing

In Partnership with
Formac Publishing Company Limited
Halifax

FOREWORD:
Why Observe the Moon?

As a boy growing up in Winnipeg, Manitoba, I caught the astronomy bug. My father took me outside one cold winter's night and pointed out the star patterns of the Big Dipper and Orion. I was hooked! I devoured all the astronomy books in the public library and drooled over the ads for fancy telescopes in *Sky & Telescope*, the only astronomy magazine available at the time. On my tenth birthday, my parents gave me a little 60-mm telescope on a wooden tripod, and an astronomy book by Patrick Moore.

That very night I started keeping a record of things I saw in my telescope (I still have the logbook — but not the telescope — more than half a century later). The first observation I wrote down was a list of craters, seas, and mountains I could find on the Moon with my little telescope. Later, I started making crude drawings of what the Moon looked like through the eyepiece. I also observed lunar eclipses, occultations of stars by the Moon, earthshine — in short, all the things described in the book you are holding in your hands now. I wish I'd had this book way back then!

Of course, I moved on from the Moon to observe stars, planets, galaxies, nebulae, and all sorts of things. I also worked my way up to using bigger telescopes. When other amateur astronomers stayed indoors "because the Moon is out ruining the sky," I was that guy sitting outside at the telescope, spending time with an old friend.

I have a unique relationship with the Moon: in the wee hours of my sixteenth birthday, astronaut Neil Armstrong stepped down from the *Eagle* lunar lander onto the surface of the Moon, the first human to do so. I watched it live on fuzzy black and white TV, then went outside and gazed at the Moon. "Holy cow," I said to myself, "there are people up there!" I will never forget that.

There are many reasons to explore the Moon (with a telescope from Earth, that is). It is our nearest neighbour in space, it's easy to find, it's bright, it has a variety of visual details to enjoy, you don't have to go anywhere special to view it (your urban yard is fine), and you don't need a fancy telescope. It's just that easy. But the best reason to observe the Moon as a beginning amateur astronomer is that you will learn how to operate your telescope and to interpret what you see. Then you will be much better prepared to go hunting for planets, double stars, galaxies, and other, more challenging objects. I assure you this is the truth!

With this book, John Read has wiped the slate clean and started from scratch. He has years of experience helping ordinary folk appreciate the night sky, and he has developed an excellent sense of what excites them. He's picked out 50 interesting lunar features that he has observed, photographed, and researched himself. I've watched him do it and can attest that he has put his heart and soul into the project. Whether you are embarking on a new lifelong hobby, or just having fun, this book is for you!

David M. F. Chapman, Emeritus Editor
RASC Observer's Handbook (2012–2016)

Formac Publishing Company Limited and Stellar Publishing recognize the support of the Province of Nova Scotia through the Department of Communities, Culture and Heritage. We are pleased to work in partnership with the Province of Nova Scotia to develop and promote our cultural resources for all Nova Scotians. We acknowledge the support of the Canada Council for the Arts, which last year invested $153 million to bring the arts to Canadians throughout the country. This project has been made possible in part by the Government of Canada.

Canadä NOVA SCOTIA   Canada Council for the Arts Conseil des Arts du Canada

Cover design: Tyler Cleroux
Cover image: Istock, Adobe Stock
Consulting editor: David M. F. Chapman

Library and Archives Canada Cataloguing in Publication

Title: 50 things to see on the moon : a first-time stargazer's guide / John A. Read.
Other titles: Fifty things to see on the moon
Names: Read, John A., author.
Description: Includes bibliographical references.

Paperback ISBN: 978-1-7327261-3-0

Amazon distribution (paperback) by Stellar Publishing, Halifax, NS, Canada.

Hardcover published by:	Hardcover distributed in Canada by:	Hardcover distributed in the US by:
Formac Publishing Company Limited	Formac Lorimer Books	Lerner Publisher Services
5502 Atlantic Street	5502 Atlantic Street	1251 Washington Ave. N.
Halifax, NS, Canada	Halifax, NS, Canada	Minneapolis, MN, USA
B3H 1G4	B3H 1G4	55401
www.formac.ca		www.lernerbooks.com

TABLE OF CONTENTS

Introduction to the Moon

About 4.5 billion years ago, in a planetary system riddled with deadly asteroids, a rocky planet orbited the young Sun. An asteroid, 7,000 km across, collided with the planet, shredding it apart and spewing debris into outer space. Under gravity's influence, the debris eventually coalesced, forming two unique worlds. The larger world we call Earth, and the smaller we call the Moon.

The Moon, Earth's neighbour, has always been a fixture in the lives of humans. The Moon stabilizes Earth's spin, causes **tides**, and lights up the night. Early humans used the Moon to determine when to plant crops, and when to harvest; they developed calendars based on the lunar cycles. In fact, we get the word "month" from the Moon.

Over time, humans invented new calendars, built skyscrapers, and discovered electricity to light up the night. For many, the Moon became nothing more than an uninteresting rock. Then, in the midst of the Cold War with the Soviet Union, a US president demanded superiority over communist domination in outer space.

"We choose to go to the Moon!"
— President John F. Kennedy, 1962

The Soviets sent many robotic spacecraft to the Moon. They were the first to successfully send a robotic probe (Luna 2), which crashed on the Moon's surface. They were the first to **orbit** the Moon and to take pictures of the Moon's **far side** (Luna 3). They were the first to safely land a probe on the Moon (Luna 9). And, by the late 1960s, they were getting close to sending humans to the Moon.

But in 1968, three astronauts — Frank Borman, William Anders, and Jim Lovell — left Earth and coasted toward the Moon. This was the historic Apollo 8 mission, the first time humans left Earth's orbit. However, their spacecraft did not include a lunar lander. Upon reaching the Moon, they spent 20 hours in lunar orbit before heading home.

Then, in 1969, an American named Neil Armstrong descended from the lunar lander and set foot on the Moon. America's Cold War enemy was watching every move. With that one small step, America had won the Space Race.

As Neil Armstrong and Buzz Aldrin climbed back into the lunar module to prepare for their trip home, an uncrewed Soviet spacecraft, named Luna 15, orbited overhead. The Soviet probe changed its trajectory, possibly to get a closer look at the American astronauts, but also to prepare for landing. But adding to the Soviets' defeat, the robotic probe then crashed into a lunar mountain, just a few hundred kilometres from Neil and Buzz.

Image of Luna, uncrewed Soviet moon lander.

Buzz Aldrin on the Moon (Neil had the camera).

The Soviets' crewed lunar program suffered several failures in the shadow of Apollo's success. Most noticeably, the failure to successfully launch the giant rocket that would boost cosmonauts into space. With Americans on the Moon, the Soviets' crewed lunar program lost political support, and was subsequently cancelled.

The Moon at a Glance

You don't need any maps to appreciate the Moon — you really don't even need a telescope or binoculars (though these definitely help). Just admiring the Moon is a joy in itself. But once you view it through a telescope, you'll notice several things straight away.

Craters — Though only one or two are visible without a telescope, there are thousands of craters on the Moon visible with a small telescope. Craters are mainly formed by asteroid or meteoroid impact, but some may be ancient collapsed volcanoes. There are two general types of craters: small, simple craters, shaped like cereal bowls; and complex craters, which are large and often have a central peak formed by the rebounding of material after a large impact.

Stellar Fact!

It was a Jesuit astronomer named Giovanni Riccioli (1598–1671) who decided to name the craters after scientists and philosophers. He started the naming process by listing the most ancient names in the north and most recent in the south. Riccioli also named the *maria*, or seas, giving them Latin names meaning tranquility, rainbows, rains, cold, vapours, and several others.

Rilles (Cracks), Rupes (Cliffs), and Valles (Valleys) — You may not notice these at first glance, but the Moon is covered in cracks, cliffs, and valleys. These features can be hundreds of kilometres long and several kilometres wide (the smallest details you can see on the Moon with a telescope are at least a few kilometres wide).

Lunar Seas — Lunar seas (*maria* in Latin, pronounced "mah-ree-ah") appear as large patches of grey on the Moon's surface, with far fewer craters than their surroundings. A sea (*mare* in Latin, pronounced "mah-ray") is formed from ancient lava flows. Scientists have measured their age at several billion years old.

How Far is the Moon?

When you look at the Moon through a telescope, it almost seems as if you can reach out and touch it. However, the Moon is an average of 384,000 km away. That's over 35 times the distance from New York City to Tokyo, Japan! If you were to drive that distance non-stop, going 90 km/h, it would take almost six months!

Earth

Moon

Lunar Mountain Ranges — Just like Earth, the Moon has mountains! Most of the Moon's mountains were formed when rock was pushed up by giant asteroid impacts, which means they were formed in a matter of minutes! The most prominent (and some say spectacular) mountain range is *Montes Apenninus*, which ranges almost 600 km long, with peaks over 5 km high.

Rays — Formed when rock and dust (called ejecta) is dislodged after a meteor impact, lunar rays appear as bright streaks emanating away from the impact zone. Some rays, like those emanating from the crater Tycho, are thousands of kilometres long! They last for millions of years.

Moon scale — The Moon is 3,475 km across, about as wide as the US. The smallest detail viewed without a telescope — a lunar sea, for example — is still about the size of Texas. Through binoculars it is possible to explore craters that are as small as 100 km in diameter, or about the size of Los Angeles county. Only when you view the Moon through a telescope do you see details as small as a few kilometres, or about the size of Manhattan Island in New York.

How to Use This Book

Lunar days — This book will follow the **phases** of the Moon from New Moon to Full Moon. This transition represents about 14 days of unique views of the Moon in the evening sky. As each day passes, an additional slice of the Moon becomes visible, with the most prominent features appearing along the **terminator**, which is the ragged north–south line along which the Sun is either rising or setting on the Moon.

Moonrise and Moonset
Although the Moon rises in the east and sets in the west every day, just like the Sun, it rises about 50 minutes later each day. If you observe the Moon at the same time every day, it would appear to move from west to east.

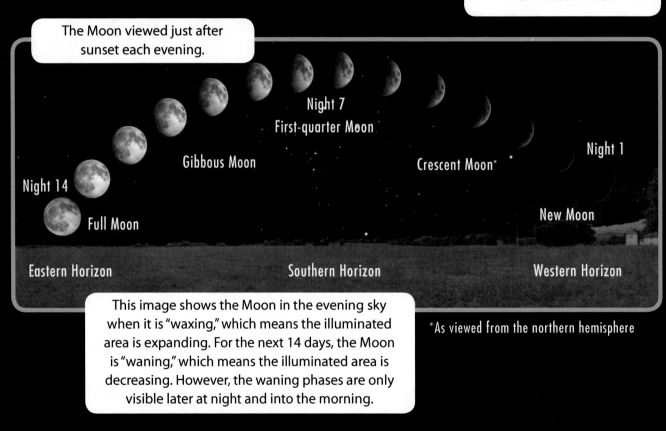

The Moon viewed just after sunset each evening.

Night 7
First-quarter Moon

Gibbous Moon

Crescent Moon*

Night 1

Night 14

Full Moon

New Moon

Eastern Horizon

Southern Horizon

Western Horizon

This image shows the Moon in the evening sky when it is "waxing," which means the illuminated area is expanding. For the next 14 days, the Moon is "waning," which means the illuminated area is decreasing. However, the waning phases are only visible later at night and into the morning.

*As viewed from the northern hemisphere

The Moon will appear differently depending on the type of telescope or binoculars you are using. These additional views will help you orient your telescope to find the more challenging targets.

You can replicate the phases of the Moon by holding a ball at arm's length at sunset and spinning in a circle. In this image, Marni Berendsen, education project coordinator at the Astronomical Society of the Pacific (ASP), does just that.

 Upright / Binoculars

 Inverted / Newtonian

 Mirror-Reversed View / Refractor

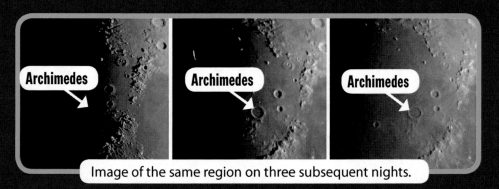

Archimedes   Archimedes   Archimedes

Image of the same region on three subsequent nights.

Each page contains three separate images of the Moon. The larger image is how the Moon looks visually or with binoculars. The other zoomed-in images are from either a Newtonian or refractor telescope. Use the image that matches your type of scope.

The terminator is the line between the Moon's night and day, and is the best place to concentrate your observing efforts. At first, the tall mountains and crater rims come into view. As the craters fill with light, walls and nearby mountains cast long shadows. Finally, once bathed in overhead light, the shadows recede and the finer details fade into hues of grey and white.

Lunar Events and How to See Them

Conjunctions — When the Moon and a star, planet, or some combination of objects appear close to each other in the sky, the event is called a "conjunction." The celestial objects are not physically close to one another, they just appear in the same general direction from Earth. Technically, a conjunction occurs when objects share the same **Right Ascension (RA)**, a term to indicate location east and west in the night sky.

Occultations — Lunar occultations occur when the Moon passes in front of a planet or a star (although only occultations of bright stars and planets are easy to observe). A list of upcoming occultations can be found online (link provided on page 80). It's often fun to observe the Moon during an occultation — you'll see the star or planet disappear at the advancing, western **limb** of the Moon (east in the sky), and reappear on the eastern limb (west in the sky) within 60 minutes.

Lunar Eclipses — When the Moon crosses into the Earth's shadow, we call this a lunar eclipse. Such an eclipse can be partial or total and can be observed over a large part of the Earth (the part that is experiencing nighttime). During an eclipse, especially during **totality** (when the Moon is fully eclipsed), the Moon appears slightly red from sunlight passing through Earth's atmosphere. Check the schedule in Appendix 1 for the dates of upcoming lunar eclipses.

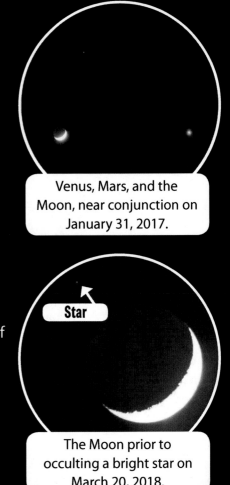

Venus, Mars, and the Moon, near conjunction on January 31, 2017.

Star

The Moon prior to occulting a bright star on March 20, 2018.

Lunar Eclipse, December 21, 2010.

Solar Eclipses — When the Earth crosses under the Moon's shadow, we call this a solar eclipse. Because the width of the Moon's shadow (about 100 km) is so much smaller than the diameter of the Earth (12,800 km), a total solar eclipse is only visible from the few places located under the shadow, which quickly moves across the surface of the Earth. The narrow shadow occurs because the Moon and Sun have approximately the same angular size in the sky. Check the eclipse schedule in Appendix 2 to see when the next solar eclipse occurs near you.

Just because you're not under the Moon's shadow doesn't mean you can't see a partial eclipse. Be sure to use commercial eclipse glasses when viewing this event.

Stellar Fact!

Not all solar eclipses are total solar eclipses. If an eclipse occurs when the Moon is farther from Earth in its orbit, it doesn't quite cover the Sun. We call this an **annular eclipse**, and you still have to be under the narrow eclipse path to see it. When the Moon covers only part of the Sun we call this a partial solar eclipse, but these are observable over a much wider area.

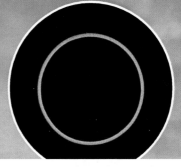

During an annular eclipse, when the Moon still doesn't fully cover the Sun's disk, we call this the "Ring of Fire." Be sure to use commercial eclipse glasses when viewing this event.

Full Moon — The lunar cycle has long functioned as a calendar of sorts and it is still used in traditional Indigenous, Asian, and Muslim calendars. You may hear names like Harvest Moon, Hunter's Moon, or **Supermoon** in the news, but from a scientific standpoint there is nothing particularly out of the ordinary about these Moons. For those who enjoy space, a Full Moon is a good time to identify all the major lunar *maria* and observe the lunar rays.

Note: Solar and lunar eclipse schedules are included in the Appendices.

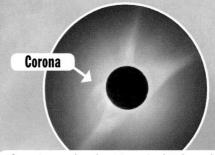

Corona

If you're under the Moon's shadow during a total solar eclipse, you experience totality. During this time you can see the Sun's corona, and even bright stars and planets.

How the Moon Appears through a Telescope or Binoculars

You may have looked at the Moon through your telescope and wondered why it appears backwards, upside down, or both! Telescopes use lenses and/or mirrors to bring light from space to your eye, but lenses turn images inside out and mirrors reverse the view! How the Moon appears in your telescope will depend on the details of its optics.

Explore Firstlight 114mm Reflector Telescope

Explore Scientific AR102 Refractor

A reflecting (Newtonian) telescope has a large concave mirror that collects the light. The light is then reflected by a diagonal mirror inside the body of the telescope, 90 degrees sideways into the eyepiece. The combination of the two reflections creates an image of the Moon that is upside down AND mirror reversed — that is, an inverted image, the same as a 180-degree rotation.

A refracting (lens-based) telescope has a large lens that collects the light. The basic refracting astronomical telescope inverts the view — that is, it reflects the image through a central point, which is the same as a 180-degree rotation. More commonly, a refractor employs a diagonal mirror or prism to reflect the image 90 degrees upwards into the eyepiece; this image of the Moon will be right side up, but will be mirror-reversed. (Some telescopes come with something called an erecting eyepiece. With this attached, the image will no longer be reversed. Spotting 'scopes, intended for nature and sports, are equipped in this way, and provide good low-power Moon views.)

90-degree diagonal

Many telescope designs use two mirrors and a star diagonal (which contains another mirror). In this case, the combination of three reflections creates a right-side-up, mirror-reversed image.

This Explore Firstlight 127mm Mak-Cassegrain telescope produces a right-side-up, mirror-reversed image, just like a refractor with a 90-degree diagonal.

Binoculars use lenses and prisms (solid glass wedges) to arrange the image to match the orientation of the unaided eye.

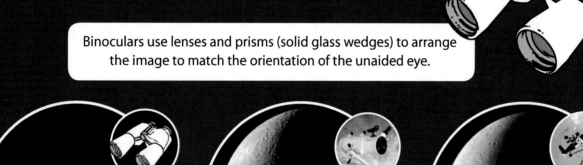

Mare Nectaris

Binocular (or naked eye) view

Mare Nectaris

Newtonian or Dobsonian view (inverted image)

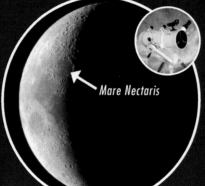

Mare Nectaris

Refractor and Schmidt-Cassegrain view with 90-degree diagonal (mirror-reversed image)

Viewing *Mare Nectaris* with binoculars, a Newtonian telescope, and a refractor telescope.

Directions on the Moon

When looking at the Moon "naturally" (as you would with unaided eyes or in binoculars, right side up and not mirror-reversed), in general terms, north is up, south is down, east is right and west is left (reversed in the southern hemisphere), as is the custom with all planetary bodies, Earth included. Note that east–west on the Moon is opposite east–west in the sky. This can be confusing! For example, as you watch the Moon in the sky during the night, it rapidly moves from east to west as the Sun and stars do. At a slower rate, the Moon moves west to east in the sky relative to the stars. When the Moon covers (or occults) a star, the star disappears behind the western limb of the Moon and reappears up to an hour later from behind it.

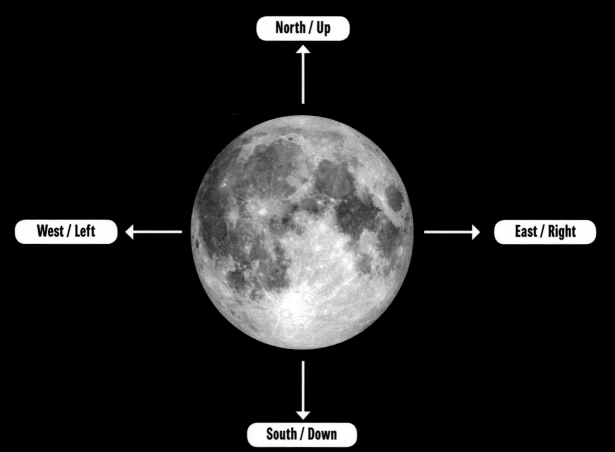

North / Up

West / Left

East / Right

South / Down

50 Things to See

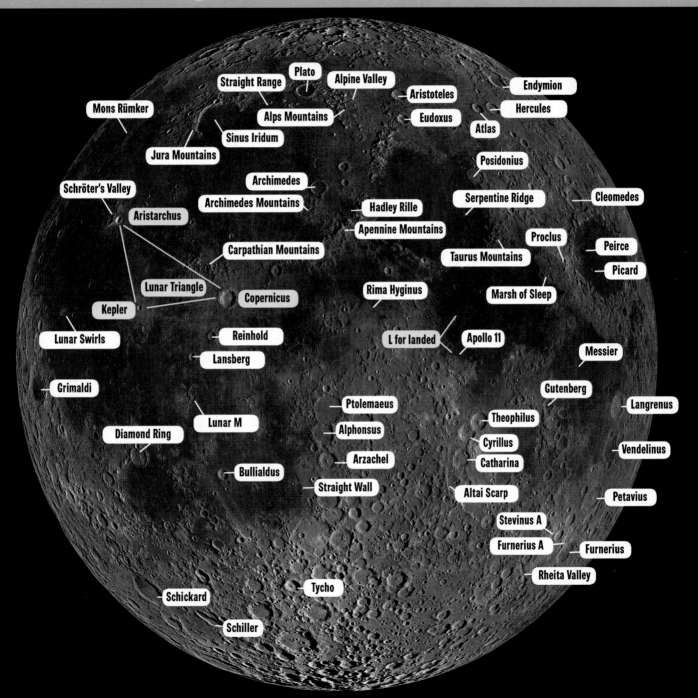

1 Lunar Seas

Though this book will progress from New Moon to Full Moon, it will help to start with an introduction to the lunar seas, since most of the items we'll encounter reside within or near these landmarks. These dark patches on the lunar surface are all several hundred kilometres across, so you can easily see them without the aid of a telescope. In fact, their shapes give rise to the traditional "Man in the Moon" visual impression. Other cultures see a rabbit, an old woman, a frog, and so on.

The seas were once thought to be actual bodies of water; however, thanks to telescopes and other scientific instruments, we now know that there is no liquid water on the surface of the Moon. The features are a result of ancient lava flows that filled basins created by asteroid impacts, appearing as dark, relatively craterless and mountainless patches. When the lava cooled, it formed dark rock called basalt. Despite this fact, the name "seas" stuck.

In Latin, the word sea is *mare* (pronounced mah-ray) and the plural is *maria* (mah-ree-ah).

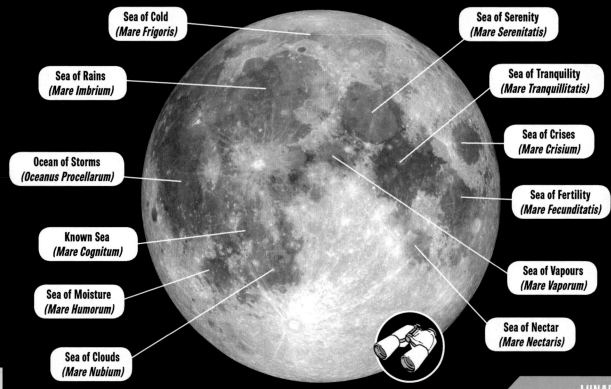

Sea of Cold
(*Mare Frigoris*)

Sea of Serenity
(*Mare Serenitatis*)

Sea of Rains
(*Mare Imbrium*)

Sea of Tranquility
(*Mare Tranquillitatis*)

Sea of Crises
(*Mare Crisium*)

Ocean of Storms
(*Oceanus Procellarum*)

Sea of Fertility
(*Mare Fecunditatis*)

Known Sea
(*Mare Cognitum*)

Sea of Vapours
(*Mare Vaporum*)

Sea of Moisture
(*Mare Humorum*)

Sea of Nectar
(*Mare Nectaris*)

Sea of Clouds
(*Mare Nubium*)

BEST VIEWED DURING
A FULL MOON
Have you seen it?

Sea of Clouds
(Mare Nubium)

Known Sea
(Mare Cognitum)

Sea of Moisture
(Mare Humorum)

Sea of Nectar
(Mare Nectaris)

Sea of Vapours
(Mare Vaporum)

Sea of Fertility
(Mare Fecunditatis)

Sea of Crises
(Mare Crisium)

Sea of Tranquility
(Mare Tranquillitatis)

Sea of Cold
(Mare Frigoris)

Sea of Serenity
(Mare Serenitatis)

Ocean of Storms
(Oceanus Procellarum)

Sea of Cold
(Mare Frigoris)

Sea of Rains
(Mare Imbrium)

Sea of Serenity
(Mare Serenitatis)

Sea of Tranquility
(Mare Tranquillitatis)

Sea of Crises
(Mare Crisium)

Sea of Fertility
(Mare Fecunditatis)

Sea of Vapours
(Mare Vaporum)

Sea of Nectar
(Mare Nectaris)

Sea of Rains
(Mare Imbrium)

Ocean of Storms
(Oceanus Procellarum)

Known Sea
(Mare Cognitum)

Sea of Moisture
(Mare Humorum)

Sea of Clouds
(Mare Nubium)

LUNAR SEAS

Days 1 to 5
Crescent Phase

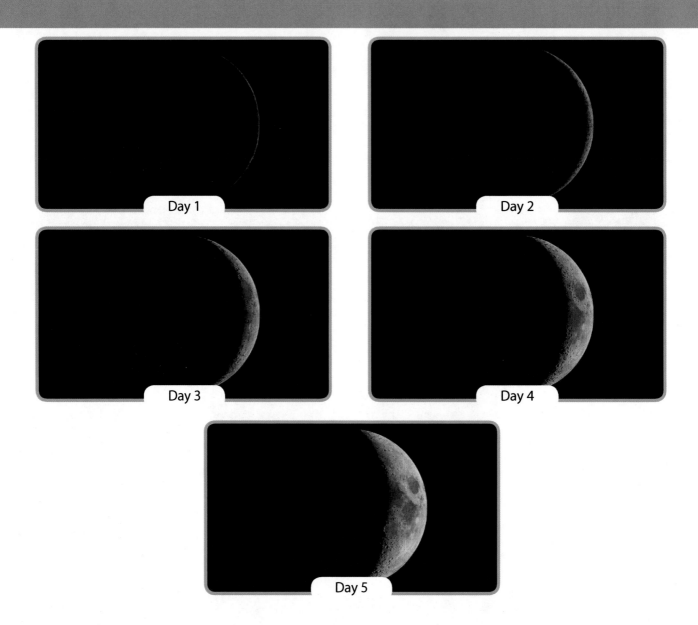

Day 1

Day 2

Day 3

Day 4

Day 5

2 Young Moon

Even though no telescope or binoculars are required to see this phase, observing a "young" Moon presents a unique challenge. You need a clear view of the western horizon, right after sunset. It doesn't get dark for a full 30 minutes after sunset, but if you wait as long as 30 minutes, it might be too late.

A clear view of the horizon can be achieved on the coast, on flat terrain, from the top of a hill, or from a tall building.

Notice that you may see the whole Moon, not only the portion that is illuminated by the Sun. This is possible because of **"earthshine,"** the light from the Sun that is reflecting off the Earth and illuminating the Moon.

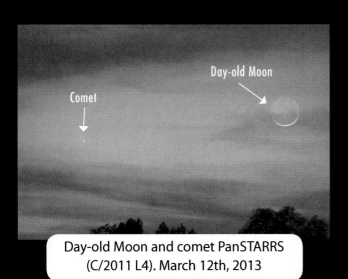

Comet

Day-old Moon

Day-old Moon and comet PanSTARRS (C/2011 L4). March 12th, 2013

VISIBLE LUNAR DAY 1
Have you seen it?

3 Gang of Four

This unofficial grouping of four large craters runs down the southeast side of the Moon. Starting with the most northerly crater, the "Gang of Four" comprises Langrenus, Vendelinus, Petavius, and Furnerius. If you look closely at Langrenus on lunar day three or four, you'll see rays stretching out to the west. The walls of Vendelinus have all but been destroyed by subsequent crater impacts, but the central depression remains. At 177 km in diameter, Petavius is the largest of the gang. In 1993, Japan's first lunar probe crashed near Furnerius.

Stellar Fact!

The nickname Gang of Four was introduced by amateur astronomer Dave North, contributor to *The Hitchhiker's Guide to the Moon* (www.shallowsky.com/moon). The moniker is now included in several lunar publications, including the RASC's Explore the Moon program.

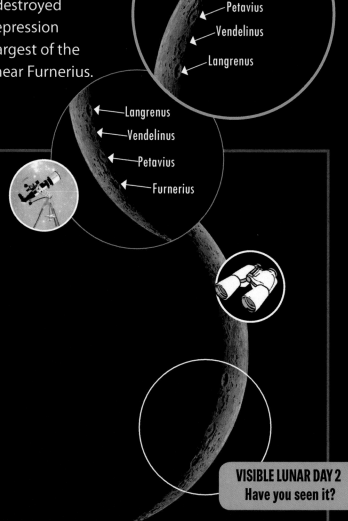

Furnerius
Petavius
Vendelinus
Langrenus

Langrenus
Vendelinus
Petavius
Furnerius

VISIBLE LUNAR DAY 2
Have you seen it?

The Japanese Hiten spacecraft that crashed in 1993.

4 Cleomedes

Just north of the Sea of Crises (*Mare Crisium*) lies the 125-km wide crater Cleomedes. This is one of the first prominent craters to appear shortly after the new Moon. Close inspection shows its eroded walls have been punctured by several younger impacts and a small central peak rises from the lava-flooded crater floor.

Stellar Fact!

Crater Cleomedes is named for a famous Greek astronomer known for writing one of the earliest books on astronomy, predating even Ptolemy's *Almagest* (history's most famous scientific text). Cleomedes's book *On the Circular Motions of the Celestial Bodies* includes the earliest description of the "Moon illusion," the optical illusion where the Full Moon appears larger (but actually isn't) when near the horizon.

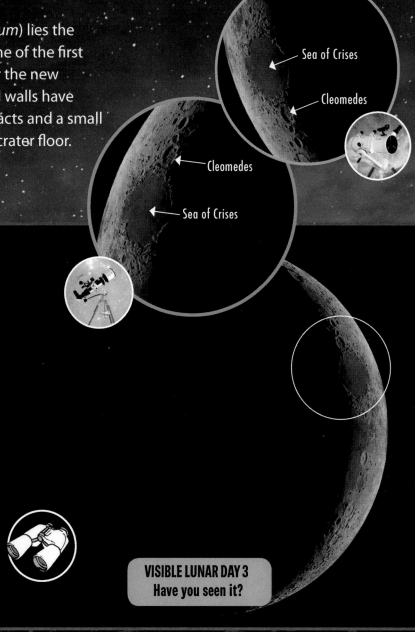

Sea of Crises

Cleomedes

Cleomedes

Sea of Crises

VISIBLE LUNAR DAY 3
Have you seen it?

5 Endymion

Endymion's floor is composed of a very light-absorbent rock, making this 125-km wide crater appear quite dark. With a large telescope, some amateur astronomers claim to be able to discern a perfect row of three smaller craters within Endymion, nicknaming them "Endymion's Triplet." These three smaller craters (still several kilometres wide) are clearly visible in photos from orbiting spacecraft.

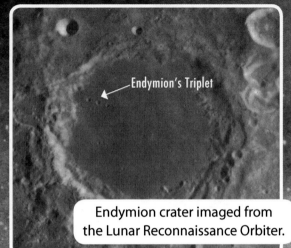

Endymion's Triplet

Endymion crater imaged from the Lunar Reconnaissance Orbiter.

Magnification

To figure out the magnification of your telescope, divide the focal length of the telescope (usually written on the telescope) by the focal length of the eyepiece (written on the eyepiece). For example, a 500-mm telescope with a 20-mm eyepiece will give a magnification of 25x.

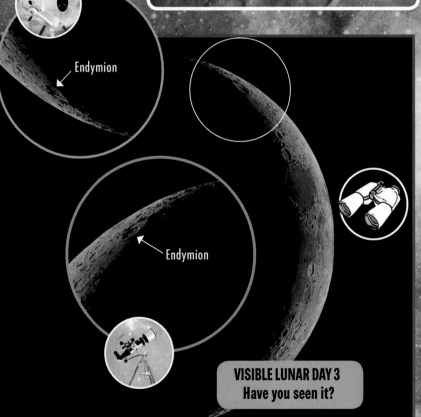

Endymion

Endymion

VISIBLE LUNAR DAY 3
Have you seen it?

6   Clock Hands

Increasing the magnification and taking a look inside the 177-km-wide crater Petavius (a member of the "Gang of Four") reveals a fascinating treasure. A giant fissure stretches from the central peak to the 8-o'clock position on the crater's wall. On the north side of the central peak, the fissure points towards 12 o'clock. These features make this a "floor-fractured crater." They were most likely formed by a buildup of magma underneath the crater, forcing the floor upward and causing it to fissure.

Minute Hand

Hour Hand

Hour Hand

Minute Hand

Stellar Fact!

Crater Petavius is named for a seventeenth-century French Jesuit scholar named Denis Pétau (*Dionysius Petavius* in Latin), known for his work in chronology — the study of the sequence of historical (or mythological) events.

CELESTRON
8 – 24mm Zoom

This object requires high magnification. A zoomable eyepiece is a great tool for the job.

VISIBLE LUNAR DAY 3
Have you seen it?

7 Emoji Craters

Looking at *Mare Crisium*, you may notice two craters that look almost like eyes in the rather barren surface of this lunar sea. Just for fun, use light and shadows on the nearby ridges to complete the face of an emoji. The craters, Peirce at 18-km wide and Picard at 23-km wide, are known as "Eratosthenian" craters, which simply means that they were formed from impacts that occurred after the formation of the lunar sea, in the same era as the crater Eratosthenes (1.1 to 3.2 billion years ago). About 100 km east of Picard in *Mare Crisium*, the Soviet Union landed two robotic spacecraft, Luna 23 (in 1974) and Luna 24 (in 1976). Luna 23 was damaged during its landing, but Luna 24 successfully returned a lunar soil sample to Earth.

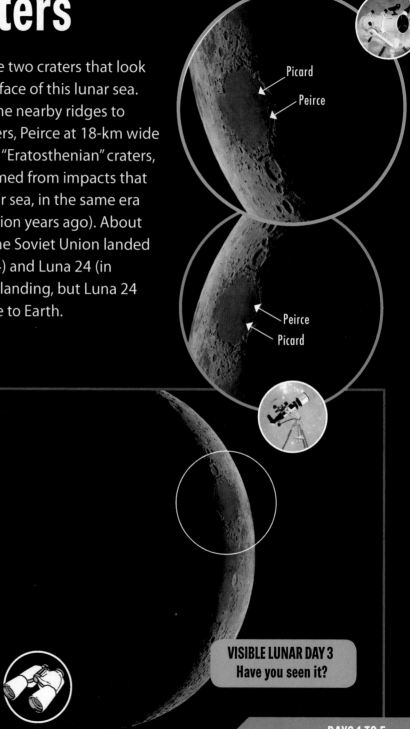

Picard
Peirce

Peirce
Picard

VISIBLE LUNAR DAY 3
Have you seen it?

Stellar Fact!

Crater Picard is named for a French astronomer named Jean-Félix Picard (who was most likely the inspiration for the Jean-Luc Picard character from *Star Trek: The Next Generation*). Jean Picard was a contemporary of Sir Isaac Newton, and was known for developing extremely accurate means of measurement. Crater Peirce is named for Benjamin Peirce, a mathematician and Harvard professor, who is known in astronomy circles for his contribution to celestial mechanics.

8 Atlas & Hercules: The Titan Craters

Atlas, with a diameter of 87 km, and Hercules, with a diameter of 71 km, are a pair of craters located at a high northern latitude. Hercules is over a kilometre deeper than Atlas, and, on lunar day three into day four, its crater floor is still cloaked in shadow. When viewing Hercules in full sunlight, you may be able to observe a small crater within the crater (Hercules G) as well as one on the rim (Hercules F).

Stellar Fact!

In Greek mythology, after losing a great battle, the titan Atlas was condemned by the god Zeus to hold up the sky. Hercules, a son of Zeus, was a hero known for his great strength.

Atlas and Hercules holding up the Earth.

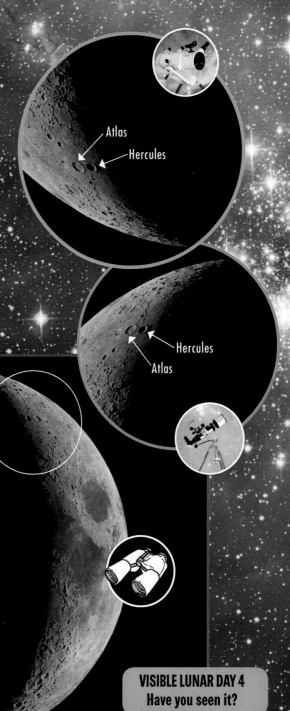

Atlas
Hercules

Hercules
Atlas

VISIBLE LUNAR DAY 4
Have you seen it?

9 Messier's Rays

Relative to the Earth and Moon, meteors and asteroids travel through space at an astonishing quarter million kilometres per hour! Craters are round because when a rock impacts at these incredible speeds, energy is released like an atomic bomb. The tiny Messier craters found near the centre of *Mare Fecunditatis*, however, are not round! It's likely the single rock that made these two craters impacted at an incredibly steep angle (between 1 and 5 degrees, based on lab experiments), breaking apart in the process. The craters, which are only about 10 km wide, feature a 120-km-long double ray that is visible even during a Full Moon.

Double Rays
Messier and Messier A

Double Rays
Messier and Messier A

Stellar Fact!

This crater is named for eighteenth-century French comet hunter Charles Messier. Messier developed a famous list of nebulae and other deep-sky objects.

VISIBLE LUNAR DAY 4
Have you seen it?

10 Wooden Shoe

During the fourth lunar day, an odd shape rises from the shadows. The Gutenberg crater lies on the southwest shore of *Mare Fecunditatis* and is particularly striking when viewed as the terminator touches the western wall. Other authors describe this crater, and surrounding structures, as a lobster's claw or a teardrop. To me, this formation looks like a shoe or a wooden clog.
What do you see?

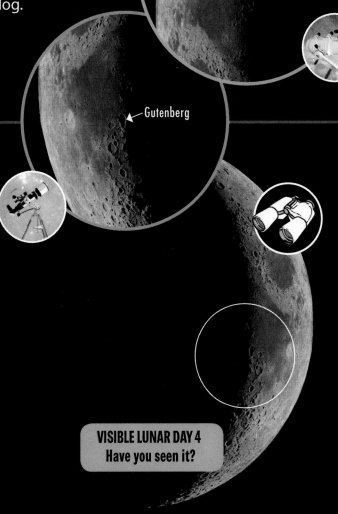

Gutenberg

Gutenberg

VISIBLE LUNAR DAY 4
Have you seen it?

Stellar Fact!

The Gutenberg crater is named for Johann Gutenberg, the inventor who brought the printing press to Europe. His innovations revolutionized the spread of information, increased literacy, laid the foundations for the scientific revolution, and are credited with ushering in the modern era.

11   Rheita Valley

On the southwest side of the Moon lies a 330-km long trench. If you were to follow this trench towards the northwest, you'd notice that it points at *Mare Nectaris*. It's possible that this valley, among others, was carved out by the explosive ejecta from the asteroid impact that made this large lunar sea.

Lunar map by Anton Maria Schyrleus of Rheita.

Stellar Fact!

Anton Maria Schyrleus of Rheita was a Czech astronomer and telescope designer. He is known for having made Johannes Kepler's telescope, and for sketching primitive maps of the Moon.

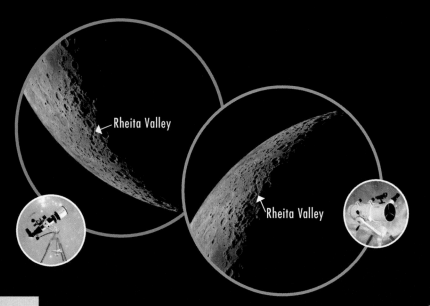

Rheita Valley

Rheita Valley

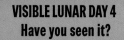

VISIBLE LUNAR DAY 4
Have you seen it?

12 Altai Scarp

The Altai Scarp is a steep hillside that spans 480 km along the rim of the Nectaris Basin. As the Moon enters day five, the hillside enters the sunlight. The light strikes these steep slopes and high peaks like a beautiful arm, reaching out into the darkness. The Altai Scarp terminates at the crater, Piccolomini. At 88 km wide, this prominent crater, with its tall central mountain, is over 4 km deep.

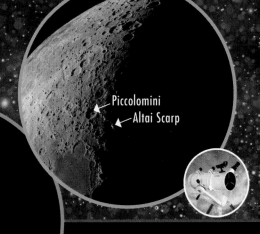

Piccolomini
Altai Scarp

Altai Scarp
Piccolomini

VISIBLE LUNAR DAY 5
Have you seen it?

Stellar Fact!

The Altai Scarp is named after the Altai Mountains, located in central Asia, bordering China, Russia, Mongolia, and Kazakhstan. In Mongolian, Altai means "Mountains of Gold."

The crater Piccolomini is named for Alessandro Piccolomini, a sixteenth-century Italian astronomer and writer known for producing the first star atlas, called *De le stelle fisse* (*On the Fixed Stars*).

13 Taurus Mountains

The Taurus Mountains extend between the two lunar seas, Serenity and Crises. A branch of the mountain range juts out between Serenity and Tranquility. This peninsula of sorts contains the Taurus–Littrow Valley, landing site of Apollo 17. Don't expect to see a lunar rover with your telescope, however. The smallest speck of detail you're able to see with a telescope is the size of Manhattan Island in New York!

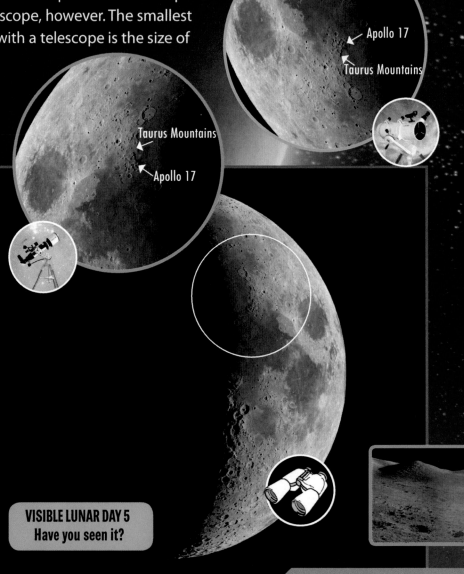

Apollo 17

Taurus Mountains

Taurus Mountains

Apollo 17

Stellar Fact!

A small valley in the Taurus Mountains called Taurus–Littrow was the 1972 landing place for Apollo 17, the most recent human mission to the Moon (as of 2018). During the astronauts' three-day stay on the Moon, Eugene Cernan and Harrison Schmitt (a geologist) covered a distance of almost 40 km in the lunar rover, conducted several scientific experiments, and collected hundreds of kilograms of rock and soil samples.

VISIBLE LUNAR DAY 5
Have you seen it?

Astronaut Harrison Schmitt stands next to a giant boulder.

Astronaut Gene Cernan takes this picture of Harrison Schmitt and the lunar rover next to a crater named "Shorty."

Astronaut Gene Cernan in the lunar rover.

14 Sea Shell Crater

This 95-km diameter crater almost looks like a sea shell, and is a fantastic crater to observe at high magnification. On close inspection, you should be able to see a small crater within the crater. With a larger telescope and excellent viewing conditions, you may be able to make out several other interesting features like fissures and small mountains.

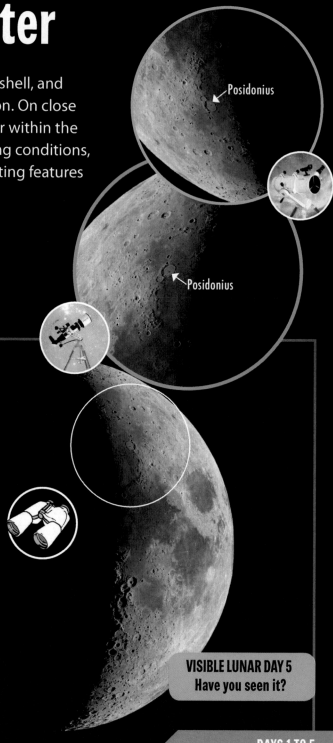

Posidonius

Posidonius

Stellar Fact!

Posidonius was a Roman philosopher who was born in the second century BCE. He was known as a polymath, someone who is an expert in numerous fields. His writings on the Moon related the lunar cycle to the tides. He also calculated the distance to the Moon and the radius of the Earth, achieving numbers close to the currently accepted values.

VISIBLE LUNAR DAY 5
Have you seen it?

15 Serpentine Ridge

The Serpentine Ridge is a pronounced 365-km wrinkle, stretching north–south across the Sea of Serenity. If you look closely, you'll see that this ridge is just part of a ring of ridges, stretching for several hundred kilometres and encircling the interior of the basin.

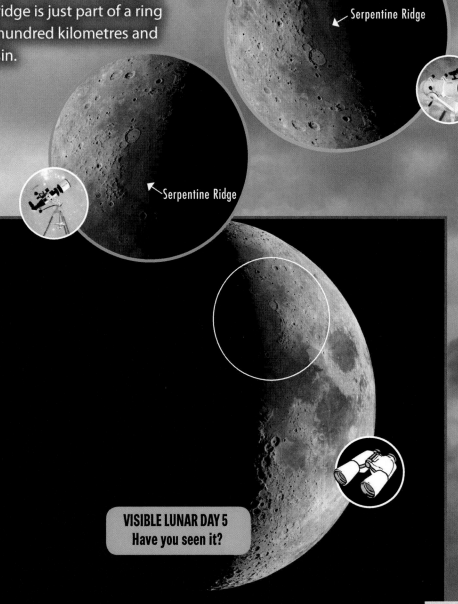

Serpentine Ridge

Serpentine Ridge

Stellar Fact!

Ridges on the Moon are typically named for geologists and the Serpentine Ridge is technically part of the Dorsa Smirnov wrinkle ridge system. However, lunar maps tend to disregard the geological name and use Serpentine Ridge instead. This is probably because the name is fitting for the Moon's most prominent wrinkle ridge, as it has the appearance of slithering snake.

VISIBLE LUNAR DAY 5
Have you seen it?

Days 6 to 8
Near First Quarter

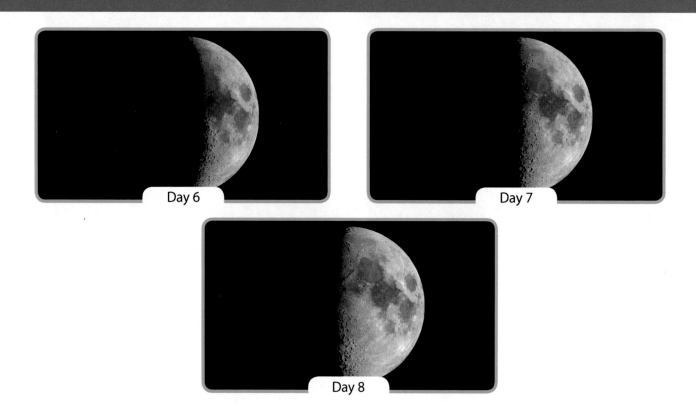

Day 6

Day 7

Day 8

16 Dumbbell Craters

Formed by the craters, Catharina (99 km wide) and Cyrillus (98 km wide), this cool formation looks like a dumbbell you might find at a gym. A third crater, Theophilus (99 km wide), borders the northeastern wall of Cyrillus, and is identified by its massive central peak. A similar feature appears in deep space: the Dumbbell Nebula (aka M27), found near the Northern Cross, is a great target for beginner stargazers.

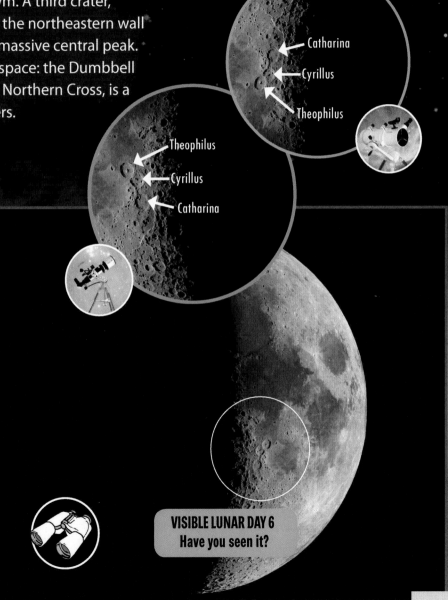

Catharina

Cyrillus

Theophilus

Theophilus

Cyrillus

Catharina

VISIBLE LUNAR DAY 6
Have you seen it?

Stellar Fact!

Catharina is named for Catherine of Alexandria, a Roman Catholic saint and martyr. However, modern scholars consider Catharine to be a legend based on Hypatia, an astronomer and the first-known female mathematician. Cyrillus is named for Saint Cyril of Alexandria, a theologian known for his translations. Theophilus was an Alexandrian pope known for destroying many pagan temples and artifacts.

17 L for Landed (Apollo 11)

On September 12, 1962, President Kennedy made his famous speech, nicknamed "We choose to go to the Moon." On July 20, 1969, Neil Armstrong and Buzz Aldrin landed the lunar module in the Sea of Tranquility, while command module pilot Michael Collins orbited the Moon. The Apollo 11 mission was the third mission to that particular location, but the first with crew on board. In 1965, a spacecraft called Ranger 5 intentionally impacted within a few dozen kilometres of the Apollo 11 site, and two years later, in 1967, a robotic spacecraft called Surveyor 5 landed nearby, taking almost 20,000 images — used, in part, for planning the human mission.

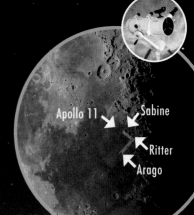

Image of a Surveyor probe.

Image of a NASA Ranger probe.

Stellar Fact!

To find the landing site, make an "L" as shown between craters Arago, Ritter, and Sabine. The bottom of the L points to the vicinity (within 90 km) of these three mission locations. Remember, you can't see any of the spacecraft. The smallest details that can be seen from Earth are about the size of Manhattan.

VISIBLE LUNAR DAY 6
Have you seen it?

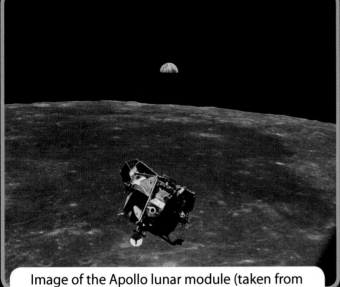

Image of the Apollo lunar module (taken from the command module) as it returns from the surface of the Moon.

Crew of Apollo 11: from left to rig[...] Neil Armstrong, Michael Collins, a[...] Edwin (Buzz) Aldrin Jr.

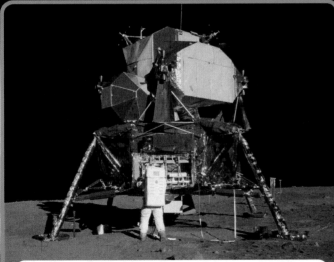

This image, taken by Armstrong, shows Buzz Aldrin at the lunar module.

Apollo 11's Saturn 5 rocket leaves the launch pad.

18 Archer's Bow

About 80 km east of the Lunar V (see page 41) lies a channel called Rima Hyginus. With a bit of searching this rille (channel), which was formed when a lava tube collapsed, can be seen through nearly any small telescope. Photographs from orbiting spacecraft show several craters within the channel. These craters are not impact craters, but are suspected to be volcanic in origin.

Rima Hyginus imaged from the Lunar Reconnaissance Orbiter.

Rima Hyginus

Rima Hyginus

Stellar Fact!

This rille and central crater get their name from Gaius Julius Hyginus, a notable first-century Roman author and scholar. Sadly, none of his works survive today.

VISIBLE LUNAR DAY 7
Have you seen it?

Neighbouring craters Aristoteles (88 km wide) and Eudoxus (70 km wide) cast deep shadows on their crater floors when the terminator is near. When viewed from the side, these craters, along with the curved mountain range to the west, almost look like a cyclist riding his bike with a dog (or bear) riding on the back.

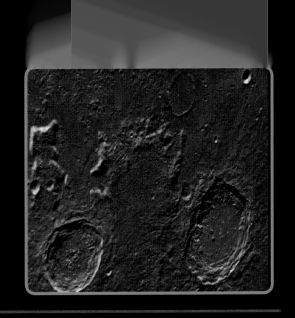

Stellar Fact!

The crater Aristoteles was named for the famous Greek philosopher, Aristotle (born 384 BCE). Eudoxus was named for Eudoxus of Cnidus (born 400 BCE), a Greek astronomer known for creating geometric models to explain the motion of the Sun, Moon, stars, and planets.

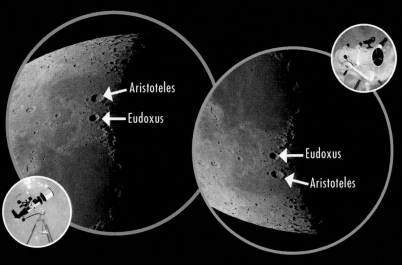

Aristoteles
Eudoxus

Eudoxus
Aristoteles

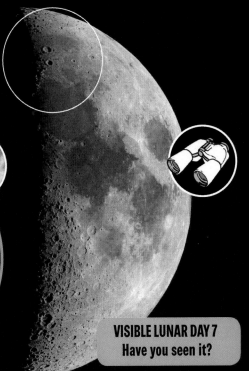

VISIBLE LUNAR DAY 7
Have you seen it?

20 Lunar X

The Lunar X, sometimes referred to as the Werner X, is a delightful target, but your timing has to be just right. The X pattern appears and disappears over a period of about four hours around the time of the first quarter phase of the lunar cycle, and it will only be visible if the Moon is visible from your location at that time. The X is neither a mountain nor a crater, but a collage of light and shadows in the ridges of three separate craters. What's the best strategy to view the X? Simply observe the Moon as often as you can around the first quarter, and you'll be bound to catch the X after a few attempts.

Online astronomy forums such as Cloudy Nights sometimes post Lunar X schedules at the beginning of the calendar year.

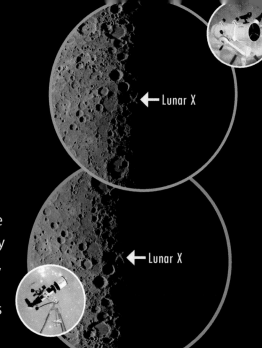

← Lunar X

← Lunar X

Stellar Fact!

The crater Werner is named for German mathematician Johannes Werner. Werner's extensive work on spherical trigonometry, a field of mathematics, is used by first- and second-year astronomy students as they learn to navigate the **celestial sphere**.

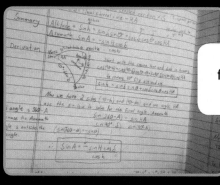

Author's notes from a second-year astrophysics class.

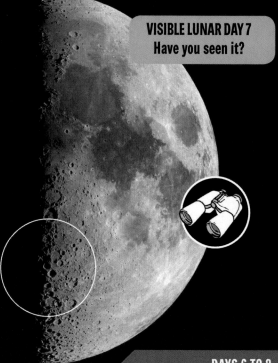

VISIBLE LUNAR DAY 7
Have you seen it?

21 Lunar V

Although visible at exactly the same time as the Lunar X, the Lunar V sticks around for quite a bit longer, though the farther away from the terminator it is, the more this feature blends into the background. In looking at a lunar map, or even photos from orbiting spacecraft, the V feature is barely discernable. Only when the light strikes the mountain peaks at a low angle is the figure most prominent.

Close-up of the Lunar V from the Lunar Reconnaissance Orbiter.

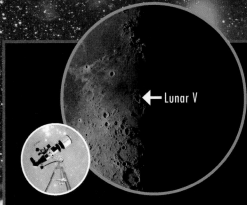

← Lunar V

← Lunar V

Stellar Fact!

The bottom of the V points in the direction of a 1967 robotic probe named Surveyor 6. This spacecraft, which landed in *Sinus Medii* (Central Bay), made history as the first spacecraft to restart its engine on the lunar surface. During a very short flight, the probe travelled to a height of about 4 m, landed, and resumed functioning.

VISIBLE LUNAR DAY 7
Have you seen it?

22 Centreline Craters

Ptolemaeus, at 153 km wide, Alphonsus, at 119 km wide, and Arzachel, at 97 km wide, form a trio of craters arcing down the Moon's prime meridian (the centreline on lunar maps). Though Alphonsus and Arzachel exhibit tall central peaks, Ptolemaeus has a surprisingly smooth crater floor. The crater Alphonsus is the location of the remains of a 1965 robotic probe called Ranger 9. This spacecraft, designed to crash into the Moon, was equipped with cameras that beamed live footage back to Earth of its descent towards the crater floor.

← Arzachel
← Alphonsus
← Ptolemaeus

← Ptolemaeus
← Alphonsus
← Arzachel

Stellar Fact!

The crater Ptolemaeus appears from Earth to be almost at the Moon's exact centre. It is fitting that this crater is named for Claudius Ptolemy. His book, the *Almagest*, written almost 1,900 years ago, placed a spherical Earth at the centre of the universe. This book would remain largely uncontested until the Copernican Revolution, 1,400 years later.

VISIBLE LUNAR DAY 8
Have you seen it?

23 Apennine Mountains

The Apennine Mountains (also known as *Montes Apenninus*) form part of the wall of the Sea of Rains (*Mare Imbrium*). At around 600 km long, it is the largest mountain range on the Moon. Some mountain peaks reach a height of well over 5 km (for comparison, Mount Everest is almost 9 km high). These mountains formed almost 4 billion years ago during the impact that formed the Imbrium Basin.

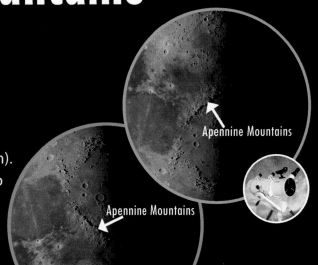

Apennine Mountains

Apennine Mountains

Stellar Fact!

The Apennine Mountains get their name from the Apennine Mountains that run down the centre of Italy.

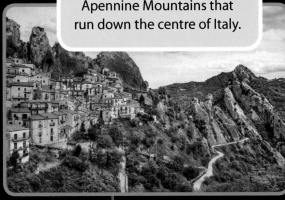

VISIBLE LUNAR DAY 8
Have you seen it?

In the summer of 1971, the Hadley Rille was a location well known by much of the world's population — nearby was the landing site of Apollo 15. The rille itself is a 130-km-long channel most likely formed by a collapsed lava tube. At just over 1 km in width, the Hadley Rille is the most challenging object in this book. The channel is almost at the visibility limit for Earth-based telescopes, but in clear skies, with a moderately good telescope and high magnification, the Hadley Rille will appear as a squiggly line within the Apennine Mountains. To find it, use the two neighbouring craters Aristillus and Autolycus in *Mare Imbrium* and follow an imaginary line down to where it intersects the mountains.

Stellar Fact!

The Hadley Rille, along with nearby mountain *Mons Hadley*, are named for English mathematician and inventor John Hadley. Hadley's inventions included improvements in telescope design and, along with inventor Thomas Godfrey, the octant — a celestial navigation aid that preceded the sextant.

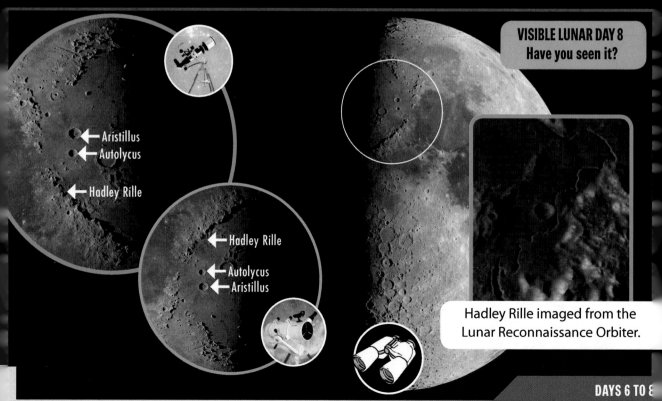

Aristillus
Autolycus
Hadley Rille

Hadley Rille
Autolycus
Aristillus

VISIBLE LUNAR DAY 8
Have you seen it?

Hadley Rille imaged from the Lunar Reconnaissance Orbiter.

DAYS 6 TO 8

Apollo 15

This photograph, by astronaut Jim Irwin, shows Dave Scott working with the lunar rover close to the Hadley Rille.

Astronaut Dave Scott sets up experiments.

Apollo 15 on the launch pad.

25 Alps Mountains

The Alps Mountains (*Montes Alpes*) form the northeastern edge of the Sea of Rains (*Mare Imbrium*) and the southern boundary of the Sea of Cold (*Mare Frigoris*). These mountains contain several prominent lunar targets, including the Alpine Valley and the crater Plato. They are particularly interesting to view during the first quarter, when half of the mountain range falls along the terminator, maximizing the shadows and contrast.

Stellar Fact!

The Alps Mountains are named for the Alps in Europe. The European Alps arc over Italy and the Mediterranean Sea in almost the same way that the lunar Alps arc over the Sea of Rains (*Mare Imbrium*).

Alps Mountains

Alps Mountains

VISIBLE LUNAR DAY 8
Have you seen it?

26 Alpine Valley

The Alpine Valley (*Vallis Alpes*) is my favourite lunar target. It appears like a giant sword, piercing the Alps Mountains. At its widest, the valley is about 10 km across, and extends over 150 km in length.

Alpine Valley

Alpine Valley

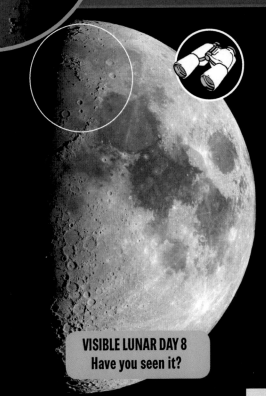

Stellar Fact!

I always imagine this valley was formed by an asteroid smashing through the mountains. However, this was not the case. The valley was most likely formed by two faults, one on either side of the valley. In geology, the valley between two faults is called a "graben." In North America, the most famous graben is responsible for Lake Tahoe, a popular tourist destination in California. Europe has an impressive graben as well — the Rhine Valley.

VISIBLE LUNAR DAY 8
Have you seen it?

27 Archimedes Crater

Archimedes is an 83-km-wide crater with a crater floor fully flooded with hardened lava. Immediately to the southwest are a cluster of mountains with the same name that are not much larger than the crater itself.

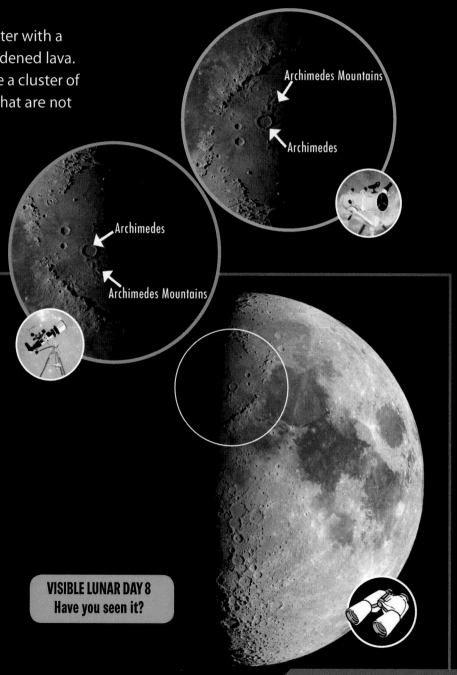

Archimedes Mountains

Archimedes

Archimedes

Archimedes Mountains

Stellar Fact!

This crater is named for the Greek mathematician known for discovering the principles of buoyancy, which led to the principle of hydrostatic equilibrium (when the outward pressure of a gas or liquid is in balance with gravity). Though his discovery primarily related to objects suspended in liquid, hydrostatic equilibrium is foundational to astrophysicists in understanding the properties of the interiors of stars.

VISIBLE LUNAR DAY 8
Have you seen it?

28 Straight Wall

One of the most popular targets for lunar observers, the Straight Wall is very pronounced on lunar day eight, when it lies less than a few hundred kilometres from the terminator. The "wall" is more like a gentle slope and isn't more than 300 m high. It's the shadow that makes this 110-km-long fault appear so pronounced.

During the waning phases, the sunlight strikes the wall from the other direction, and instead of a shadow, we see an illuminated cliff face.

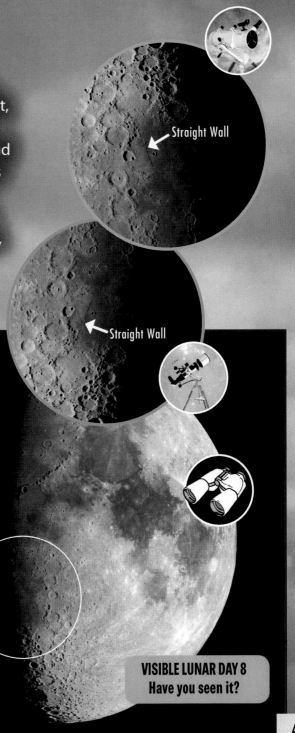

Straight Wall

Straight Wall

Stellar Fact!

The Straight Wall is officially known as *Rupes Recta*. The small 17-km-wide crater next to it is named "Birt" with 7-km-wide "Birt A" resting near Birt's crater wall. Birt is named for nineteenth-century astronomer William Radcliffe Birt, a colleague of famous astronomer William Herschel.

VISIBLE LUNAR DAY 8
Have you seen it?

Days 9 to 13
Waxing Gibbous Phase

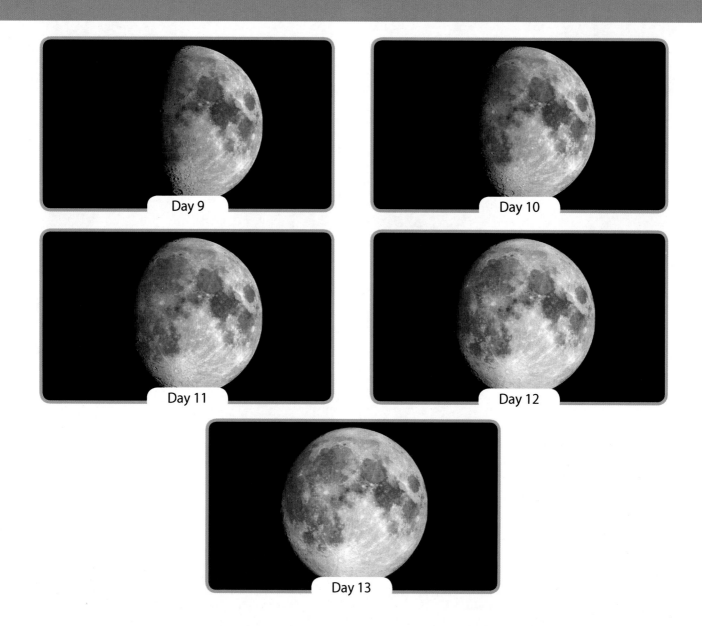

Day 9

Day 10

Day 11

Day 12

Day 13

29 Swiss Cheese Crater

At 225 km in diameter, Clavius is the third-largest crater on the Earth-facing side of the Moon and, like all larger craters, has several smaller craters within. The pattern of interior craters is quite striking. Starting in the east, the craters decrease in size as they follow an arcing path to the west. Fans of science fiction may remember this crater from the movie *2001: A Space Odyssey*, as it was the location of the Lunar Administrative Facility.

Clavius

Clavius

Stellar Fact!

The Clavius crater is named for Christopher Clavius, a German astronomer and mathematician. Clavius got to use telescopes very shortly after their invention, and he marvelled at the sheer number of stars they revealed. He observed the satellites of Jupiter, and even commented on Saturn's rings, which (due to poor optics) he believed were stars attached to the left and right side of the planet.

VISIBLE LUNAR DAY 9
Have you seen it?

30 Plato Crater

Nestled in the Alps Mountains, Plato is a very prominent crater, 101 km across. Plato's defining feature is that its floor is dark and nearly featureless — only a few small craters are visible at high magnification. Look closely and you'll see a triangular formation on the western wall. This is a section of the crater wall that broke off and slid inward. In geology, this type of formation is called a "massif."

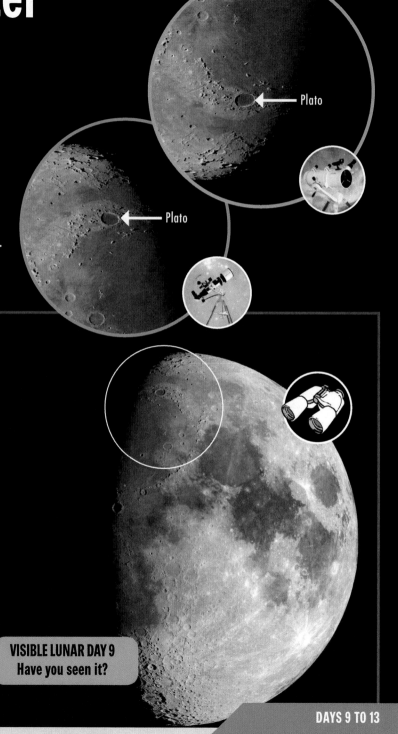

Plato

Plato

Stellar Fact!

This crater was named for the famous Greek philosopher Plato, a man who lived around 2,400 years ago. Plato's work, along with his teacher Socrates and his student Aristotle, set the stage for the process we now know as science. Plato established a school and called it the Academy, which formed the basis for the term "academia."

VISIBLE LUNAR DAY 9
Have you seen it?

31 Librarian's Crater

At the southern tip of the Appennine Mountains lies this deep crater, 59 km across. The crater is over 3.5 km deep and its floor remains in shadow for a while after the terminator crosses the crater around lunar day eight. Once fully immersed in sunlight on day nine, you'll see a prominent central peak and terraced walls.

Eratosthenes

Eratosthenes

Stellar Fact!

Eratosthenes is named for the Greek mathematician and astronomer who first determined the circumference of the Earth. His idea was to measure the length of a shadow in two cities located a known distance apart. He used a city named Syene (Aswan), where on summer solstice the Sun is directly overhead and casts no shadow on a vertical rod. At the same time in Alexandria, a city to the north, he measured a seven-degree angle in the shadow. Knowing the distance between the cities, and the difference in the shadow's angle, Eratosthenes was able to calculate the circumference of the Earth to within 10 per cent of the accepted value. Because of his great contributions to so many fields, Eratosthenes was named director of the Library of Alexandria.

VISIBLE LUNAR DAY 9
Have you seen it?

32 Lunar M (Riphaeus Mountains)

At only 150 km long, this small but prominent mountain range separates the Ocean of Storms (*Oceanus Procellarum*) and the sea that has become known as *Mare Cognitum*. The Riphaeus Mountains are an easy target to identify, since they look like a handwritten lower case μ or Mu (m in the Greek alphabet) in a mirror-reversed view.

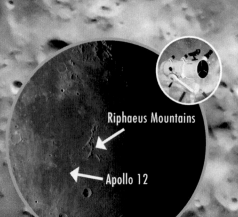

Riphaeus Mountains

Apollo 12

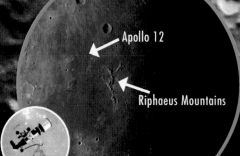

Apollo 12

Riphaeus Mountains

Stellar Fact!

On November 19, 1969, Apollo 12 astronauts Pete Conrad and Alan Bean landed 100 km north of the Riphaeus Mountains. This was the second Apollo mission to land humans on the Moon. Conrad, the lunar module pilot, made a pinpoint landing within 160 m of another spacecraft, Surveyor 3.

VISIBLE LUNAR DAY 10
Have you seen it?

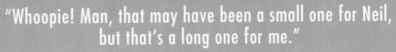

"Whoopie! Man, that may have been a small one for Neil, but that's a long one for me."
— Pete Conrad's first words from the lunar surface, spoken as he dropped down from the lander's ladder.

Alan Bean and Surveyor 3.

Alan Bean descends from the lunar module.

Apollo 12 launched in less-than-optimal weather. The rocket was struck by lightning during the launch (something that frequently happens to airplanes). This caused several of the flight instruments to reset, but everything (thankfully) returned to normal.

33 Straight Range

The Straight Range is a 90-km-long mountain range rising almost 2 km at the northern edge of *Mare Imbrium* (Sea of Rains). These mountains, along with three others, are the remains of the inner basin wall of this lunar sea.

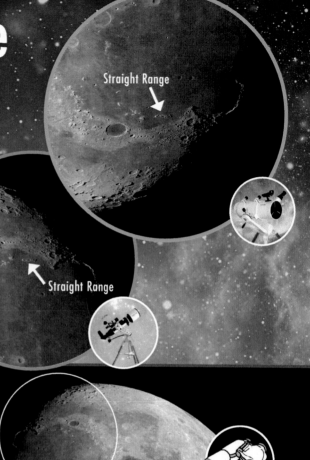

Straight Range

Straight Range

China's Yutu (Jade Rabbit) rover photographed from the Chang'e 3 robotic lander.

Stellar Fact!

Just 100 km south of this formation lies the landing zone of China's first robotic lunar rover. The spacecraft, Chang'e 3, was named for a Moon goddess from Chinese mythology, while the rover's name was *Yutu*, which means Jade Rabbit, a pet of the goddess.

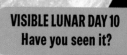

VISIBLE LUNAR DAY 10
Have you seen it?

34 Copernicus Crater

The crater Copernicus produces some of the brightest rays on the entire Moon, second only to Tycho. However, when Copernicus is viewed on day nine when close to the terminator, the rays are barely visible. Instead, observe the central peaks and terraced walls.

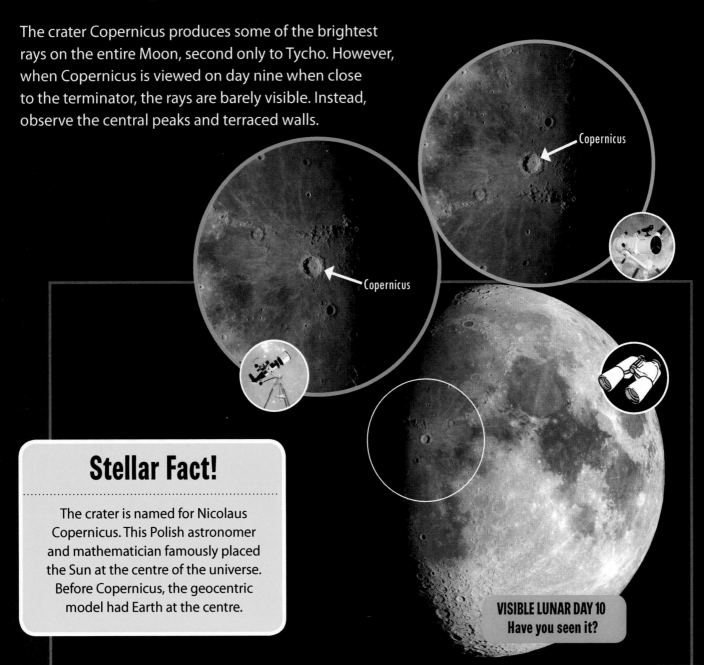

Copernicus

Copernicus

Stellar Fact!

The crater is named for Nicolaus Copernicus. This Polish astronomer and mathematician famously placed the Sun at the centre of the universe. Before Copernicus, the geocentric model had Earth at the centre.

VISIBLE LUNAR DAY 10
Have you seen it?

35 Zigzag Mountains

The Carpathian Mountains (*Montes Carpatus*) are found near Copernicus, at the southern end of the Sea of Rains (*Mare Imbrium*). This 400-km-long range seems to zigzag across the terrain, punctuated by only a few small craters. The largest crater in the range, T. Mayer, is only 33 km across.

Carpathian Mountains

Carpathian Mountains

Stellar Fact!

The earthly Carpathian Mountains arc through seven different countries in eastern Europe. The name of these mountains was first recorded by Claudius Ptolemy in a second-century atlas for the Roman Empire. Ptolemy was the Roman astronomer and geographer for whom the crater Ptolemaeus was named.

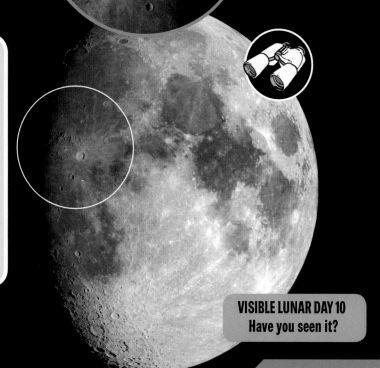

VISIBLE LUNAR DAY 10
Have you seen it?

36 Caped Crater

Bullialdus is a prominent 61-km-wide crater on the western edge of the Sea of Clouds (*Mare Nubium*). The crater has a pronounced ejecta blanket — dirt and rock thrown up by the original impact. The blanket is more rugged on one side than the other, giving itthe appearance of a hero's cape viewed from above. The two nearby craters to the south are simply named Bullialdus A (26 km across) and Bullialdus B (21 km across).

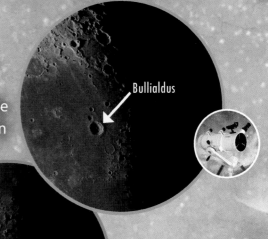

Bullialdus

Bullialdus

Stellar Fact!

Bullialdus is named for French astronomer and priest Ismaël Bullialdus, known for his 1645 book *Astronomia Philolaica*. Bullialdus went to great lengths to reconcile the observation that planets travel around the Sun in ellipses (a concept he accepted) with the previously accepted notion that planets must travel in circles (a concept grounded purely in religion).

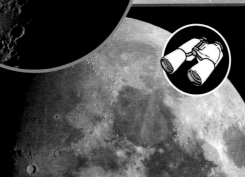

VISIBLE LUNAR DAY 10
Have you seen it?

37 Two Islands

This pair of similarly sized craters appears around day nine near the Copernicus crater in a recently named region called the Sea of Islands (*Mare Insularum*). At 48 km wide, Reinhold is larger than 39-km-wide Lansberg. About halfway between these two craters rests the long-lost impact site of the Apollo 16 third-stage booster (S-IVB). After accelerating the Apollo spacecraft to the appropriate velocity, the boosters were jettisoned and intentionally piloted into the Moon as part of a seismic wave experiment. The S-IVB struck the lunar surface at several thousand kilometres per hour, forming craters about 40 m wide (they would need to be about 50 times wider to be visible from Earth). The Apollo 16 S-IVB crater was discovered in 2015 by NASA's Lunar Reconnaissance Orbiter.

Saturn 5, third stage.

Stellar Fact!

The crater Reinhold is named for German astronomer Erasmus Reinhold, while Lansberg is named for Dutch astronomer, Johan Philip Lansberge.

Copernicus
Reinhold
Lansberg

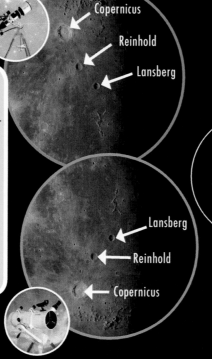

Lansberg
Reinhold
Copernicus

VISIBLE LUNAR DAY 10
Have you seen it?

38 Kepler's Rays

Kepler, a crater 29 km across, is one of three "ray" craters near the Moon's western limb. It has so many rays (I count at least ten separate segments) that it almost looks like a child's drawing of the Sun. During the Full Moon, these form part of the lunar triangle mentioned in the Full Moon section.

Kepler's Three Laws (paraphrased):

1. Planets move in elliptical orbits with the Sun at one focus.
2. Planets sweep out equal areas in equal time.
3. The square of a planet's revolution period T (in years) is equal to the cube of its semi-major axis a (in astronomical units, the average radius of Earth's orbit); that is, $T^2 = a^3$.

Stellar Fact!

Kepler is named for Johannes Kepler, one of the most important figures in the history of astronomy. Using data from astronomer Tycho Brahe, Kepler developed the famous three laws of planetary motion. These laws, in combination with Newton's law of universal gravitation, are fundamental to our understanding of planetary orbits and in calculating the orbits of spacecraft we send into deep space. Astrophysics students use Kepler's third law all the time.

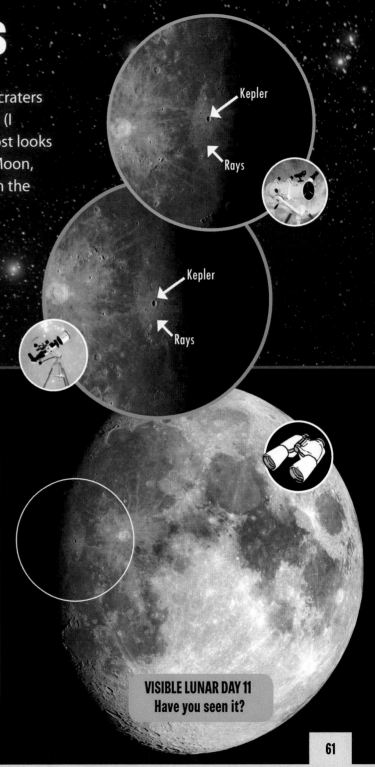

Kepler

Rays

Kepler

Rays

VISIBLE LUNAR DAY 11
Have you seen it?

39 Diamond Ring

Nicknamed "the Diamond Ring," Gassendi is a complex 110-km-wide crater with a floor punctuated by several hills and clefts criss-crossing in every direction. The companion crater, Gassendi A, makes up the diamond on the ring. Gassendi A is 33 km across, but with high crater walls, this smaller crater is twice as deep as Gassendi.

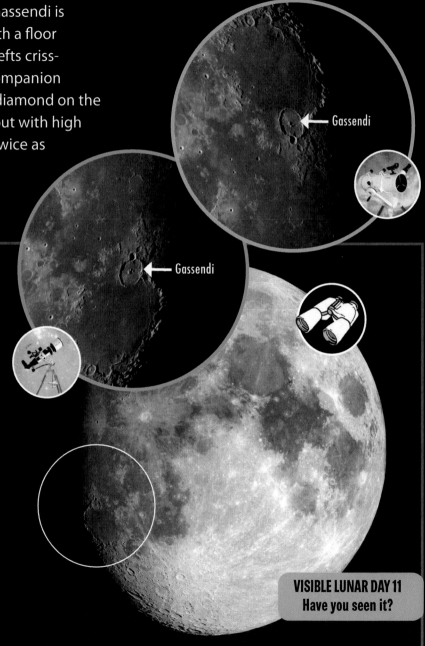

Gassendi

Gassendi

Stellar Fact!

This crater is named for Pierre Gassendi, a seventeenth-century French astronomer and philosopher. Gassendi received telescope equipment from Galileo, using it to take careful observations of the positions of the planets. He was the first person to watch Mercury transit across the Sun, an event that occurs once or twice per decade.

VISIBLE LUNAR DAY 11
Have you seen it?

40 Bay of Rainbows

Visible even with binoculars, the Bay of Rainbows (*Sinus Iridum*) rests at the northwest corner of the Sea of Rains (*Mare Imbrium*). The Jura Mountains surround the bay, arcing out into the lunar sea at two points, or "promontoria," named Laplace in the north and Heraclides in the south. About 50 km south of Heraclides rests the landing spot of an uncrewed Soviet space probe from 1970. The probe was named Luna 17, and it included an eight-wheeled lunar rover named Lunokhod 1. The Soviets piloted this rover for 322 days, over which time it travelled over 10 km.

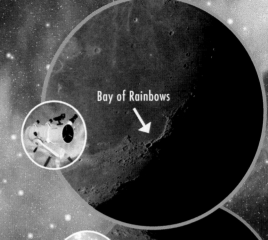

Bay of Rainbows

Bay of Rainbows

Soviet rover, Lunokhod 1.

Stellar Fact!

The mountains surrounding this bay get their name from the Jura Mountains located between France and Switzerland, part of the western Alps.

VISIBLE LUNAR DAY 11
Have you seen it?

41 Pickle Crater

Craters are almost always circular. Only a very shallow impact will create an elongated shape. This unique crater is anything but a circle. At 179 km long and only 71 km wide, this could have been the result of two asteroids impacting at very low angles. Sometime after the impact(s), lava rose up into the crater floor, combining the craters into one elongated depression.

Stellar Fact!

The crater Schiller is named for Julius Schiller, author of the 1627 book *Coelum Stellatum Christianum (A Christian Atlas of the Sky)*. In this book, Schiller attempted to replace all the classical constellations, which are based on Greek and Roman mythology, with Christian symbols and bible characters.

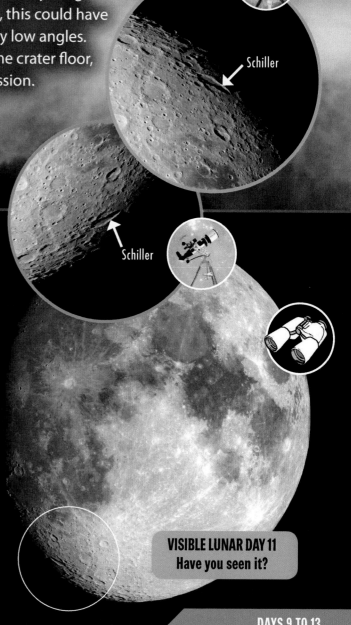

Schiller

Schiller

VISIBLE LUNAR DAY 11
Have you seen it?

A page from *Coelum Stellatum Christianum*.

42 Cobra Head

Around day 12 of the lunar cycle, one of the most interesting features on the Moon appears. Immediately west of the bright crater Aristarchus lies the prominent Schröter's Valley. A flooded crater called Herodotus rests at the end of the valley like a cobra's head.

Aristarchus is only about 40 km across, but appears as one of the brightest craters on the Moon. When we talk about brightness of the lunar surface, we're actually talking about the **albedo** — the reflective properties of various lunar rocks and dust. For example, rock containing lots of iron appears dark, whereas **breccia**, which has glasslike properties, is more reflective.

Stellar Fact!

Aristarchus, a Greek astronomer, lived in the third century BCE and was one of the first people to propose a model of the universe that centred on the Sun. However, since he lived long before the invention of the telescope, his hypotheses were impossible to test and a geocentric (Earth-centred) model of the universe dominated for nearly 1,800 more years. Schröter's Valley is named for Johann Hieronymus Schröter, known for studying the topography of the Moon and Mars.

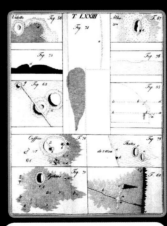

Schröter's maps of lunar features.

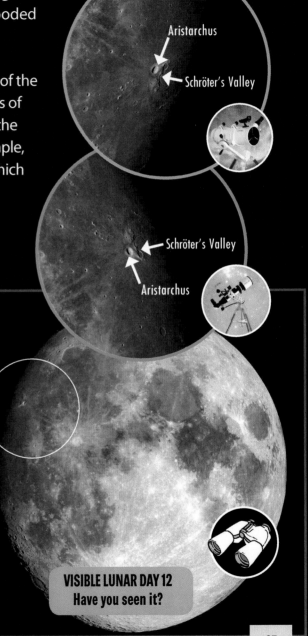

Aristarchus

Schröter's Valley

Schröter's Valley

Aristarchus

VISIBLE LUNAR DAY 12
Have you seen it?

At 227 km across, Schickard is quite large. The crater is circular, even though it appears elongated. This is because it is located near the Moon's limb (the edge of the visible part of the Moon) and we're viewing it from such a low angle. This crater's floor is only partially flooded with lava, which gives it a textured look with both bright and dark patches.

Schickard viewed from directly overhead by the Lunar Reconnaissance Orbiter.

Stellar Fact!

This crater was named for a German professor and inventor named Wilhelm Schickard. Schickard was a friend of Johannes Kepler, the man who famously developed the laws of planetary motion. Schickard is credited with designing mechanical calculating machines for mathematics and orbital mechanics.

Schickard

Schickard

Painting of Wilhelm Schickard holding a mechanical model of the solar system.

VISIBLE LUNAR DAY 12
Have you seen it?

44 Lunar Swirls

These strange patterns on the lunar surface appear almost like mixed paints on a palette. The features are completely flat and therefore cast no shadow. Scientists have proposed several models to explain these features; most hypotheses involve local magnetic fields or solar winds influencing electrically charged dust particles. These features are found in numerous locations on the Moon, but the most interesting and most prominent swirl formation is called Reiner Gamma, located just west of crater Reiner (which lies about 500 km west of the Kepler crater).

Image of the lunar swirl Reiner Gamma taken from the Lunar Reconnaissance Orbiter.

Stellar Fact!

The swirl Reiner Gamma, associated with the nearby crater Reiner, is named for Italian astronomer Vincentio Reinieri. Reinieri was a pupil of Galileo and improved upon Galileo's observations of Jupiter's moons.

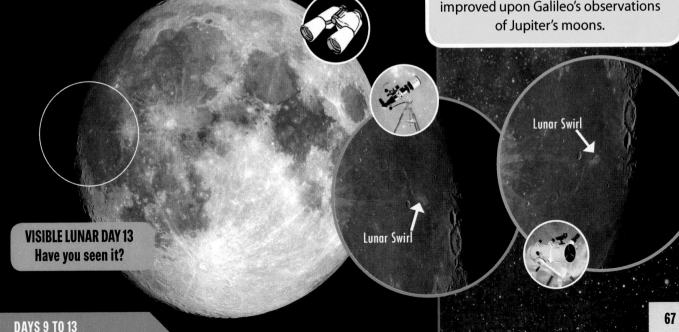

Lunar Swirl

Lunar Swirl

VISIBLE LUNAR DAY 13
Have you seen it?

45 Dome of Domes

Near the northwestern limb lies a 73-km-wide mound, almost like an inside-out crater. The lumpy dome-shaped volcanic complex, named *Mons Rümker*, is accented by several smaller domes. This object can only be seen around lunar day 13, when the terminator approaches the western limb. Once the Sun rises high at this location, the structure blends in with its surroundings. The Moon's **libration** will also affect the visibility of this object.

Mons Rümker

Mons Rümker

Stellar Fact!

This formation is named for German astronomer and director of the Hamburg Observatory, Karl Rümker. Rümker lived from 1788 to 1862, and as such is one of the most recent individuals to have a large near-side lunar formation named after him.

VISIBLE LUNAR DAY 13
Have you seen it?

46 Grimaldi: The Dark-Floored Crater

Grimaldi is a lunar basin (large dark-floored crater) best seen in the days leading up to and a few days after the Full Moon. Like a lunar sea, its dark floor is in stark contrast to the brighter craters and mountains surrounding it, so much so that this 172-km-wide crater is clearly visible through binoculars.

Grimaldi and Riccioli's selenograph.

Stellar Fact!

This crater is named for Francesco Maria Grimaldi, a seventeenth-century Jesuit priest and astronomer. Grimaldi, along with Giovanni Riccioli, created a lunar map called a **selenograph**. This lunar map was used to choose the names of the lunar craters. Given that Grimaldi and Riccioli were both priests, it's not surprising that over three dozen other Jesuit priests (most of whom were also scientists) are honoured with craters in their name.

Grimaldi

Grimaldi

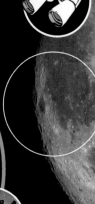

VISIBLE LUNAR DAY 13
Have you seen it?

Day 14
Full Moon

When the Moon is full, take the time to have another look at the craters and objects you've viewed over the past 13 days of the lunar cycle. Most of these objects are awash with sunlight and many are all but invisible in the near-blinding light of the Full Moon. However, some features seem to transform in direct sunlight, their reflective properties enhancing previously unexplored regions of the lunar surface.

47 Tycho

Though you can see this 85-km-wide crater as early as lunar day eight, Tycho doesn't shine until several days later and is in its glory during the Full Moon, when its ejecta arcs across much of the Moon's disk. In 1968, NASA landed a robotic spacecraft called Surveyor 7 on the rim of this crater. Armed with a video camera, this mission was the last robotic mission to the Moon before astronauts arrived in 1969.

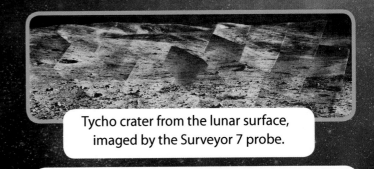

Tycho crater from the lunar surface, imaged by the Surveyor 7 probe.

Stellar Fact!

Tycho is named for sixteenth-century Danish astronomer Tycho Brahe. Tycho's highly accurate measurements of the positions of the planets enabled Johannes Kepler to develop the three laws of planetary motion. Tycho died in 1601, just seven years before the invention of the telescope.

Engraving of Tycho Brahe at the Museum of Fine Arts, Houston.

VISIBLE LUNAR DAY 14
Have you seen it?

Tycho

48 Lunar Triangle

The Lunar Triangle is visible during the day prior, and several days after, the Full Moon. It is formed by the intersection of the rays from a trio of craters: Kepler, Copernicus, and Aristarchus.

It is fitting that these three craters are tied together with rays in the same way that the men they are named after are bound together in history. We call the fifteenth-century shift towards a Sun-centred universe the "Copernican revolution." However, Copernicus believed he was simply returning to ancient wisdom, as it was Aristarchus, 1,800 years earlier, who had originally promoted the idea that Earth was not the centre of the solar system.

A generation later, Kepler devised his laws and laid the mathematical foundation that beautifully solidified the idea that the Earth and planets orbit the Sun.

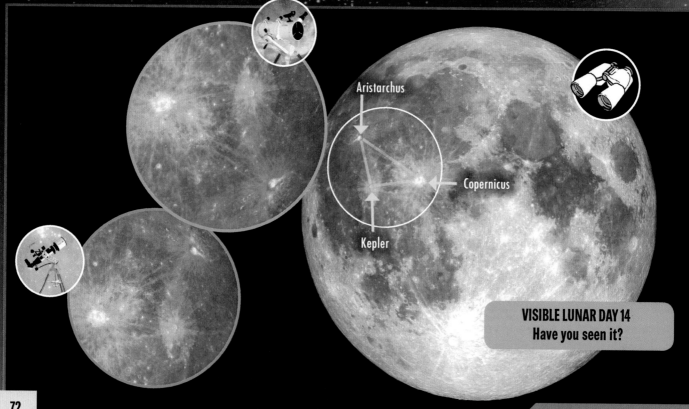

Aristarchus

Copernicus

Kepler

VISIBLE LUNAR DAY 14
Have you seen it?

The 10-km-wide Furnerius A crater is a satellite crater adjacent to one of the "Gang of Four." It is joined by a tiny 8-km-wide crater, Stevinus A. These two craters are extremely bright during the Full Moon, each with prominent rays that extend over 100 km across the lunar surface.

Stellar Fact!

Stevinus A (and its parent crater, Stevinus) are named for a Flemish engineer called Simon Stevin, known for applying the laws of physics and mathematics to engineering problems. Perhaps his most impressive invention was the land yacht — a chariot powered by wind that travelled at high speed along the beach.

A land yacht invented by Stevin around the year 1600.

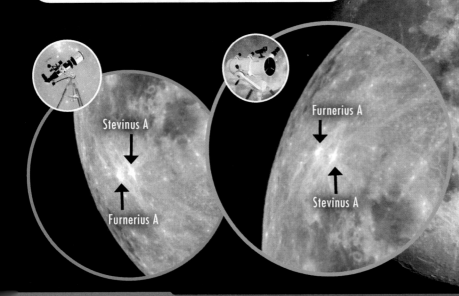

Stevinus A

Furnerius A

Furnerius A

Stevinus A

VISIBLE LUNAR DAY 14
Have you seen it?

50 Marsh of Sleep

Take a look at tiny 28-km-wide crater Proclus. When it appears during the waxing crescent phase, it is barely noticeable. At Full Moon, it's one of the brightest craters, with ejecta projecting in a fan-like pattern onto nearby mountains and seas. If you look closely, you'll notice that right below Proclus, a part of the lunar sea called the "Marsh of Sleep" (*Palus Somni*) appears. This area is much brighter (it has a high albedo) than the Sea of Tranquility on the marsh's southwestern border.

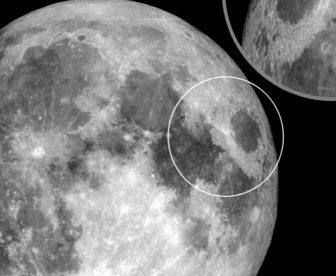

Marsh of Sleep

Proclus

Proclus

Marsh of Sleep

Stellar Fact!

Proclus is named for ancient philosopher Proclus Lycaeus who lived in the fifth century AD. Proclus is most famous for his commentaries on earlier philosophers such as Plato, and for being the head of the Platonic Academy in Athens for almost 50 years.

VISIBLE LUNAR DAY 14
Have you seen it?

Notable Features on the Far Side of the Moon

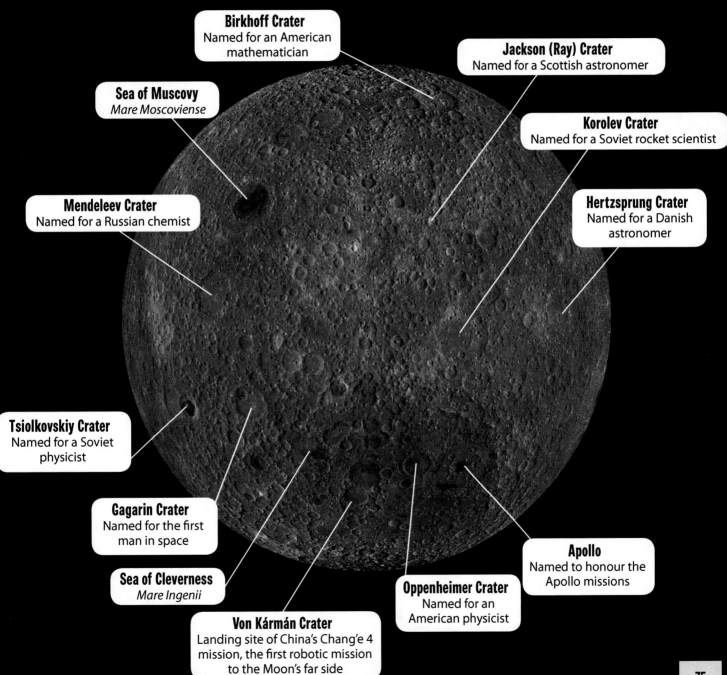

Birkhoff Crater
Named for an American mathematician

Jackson (Ray) Crater
Named for a Scottish astronomer

Sea of Muscovy
Mare Moscoviense

Korolev Crater
Named for a Soviet rocket scientist

Mendeleev Crater
Named for a Russian chemist

Hertzsprung Crater
Named for a Danish astronomer

Tsiolkovskiy Crater
Named for a Soviet physicist

Gagarin Crater
Named for the first man in space

Sea of Cleverness
Mare Ingenii

Von Kármán Crater
Landing site of China's Chang'e 4 mission, the first robotic mission to the Moon's far side

Oppenheimer Crater
Named for an American physicist

Apollo
Named to honour the Apollo missions

Appendix 1
Lunar Eclipse Schedule

CALENDAR DATE	ECLIPSE TYPE	GREATEST ECLIPSE TIME (UT ~ UTC)	ECLIPSE DURATION	GEOGRAPHIC REGION OF ECLIPSE VISIBILITY
July 16, 2019	Partial	21:32	2h 58m	South America, Europe, Africa, Asia, Australia
May 26, 2021	Total	11:20	3h 07m	East Asia, Australia, Pacific, Americas
November 19, 2021	Partial	9:04	3h 28m	Americas, Northern Europe, East Asia, Australia, Pacific
May 16, 2022	Total	4:13	3h 27m	Americas, Europe, Africa
November 8, 2022	Total	11:00	3h 40m	Asia, Australia, Pacific, Americas
October 28, 2023	Partial	20:15	1h 17m	Eastern Americas, Europe, Africa, Asia, Australia
September 18, 2024	Partial	2:45	1h 03m	Americas, Europe, Africa
March 14, 2025	Total	7:00	3h 38m	Pacific, Americas, Western Europe, Western Africa
September 7, 2025	Total	18:13	3h 29m	Europe, Africa, Asia, Australia
March 3, 2026	Total	11:35	3h 27m	East Asia, Australia, Pacific, Americas
August 28, 2026	Partial	4:14	3h 18m	East Pacific, Americas, Europe, Africa
January 12, 2028	Partial	4:14	0h 56m	Americas, Europe, Africa
July 6, 2028	Partial	18:21	2h 21m	Europe, Africa, Asia, Australia
December 31, 2028	Total	16:53	3h 29m	Europe, Africa, Asia, Australia, Pacific
January 26, 2029	Total	3:23	3h 40m	Americas, Europe, Africa, Middle East
December 20, 2029	Total	22:43	3h 33m	Americas, Europe, Africa, Asia
June 15, 2030	Partial	18:35	2h 24m	Europe, Africa, Asia, Australia

Eclipse Predictions by Fred Espenak, NASA's Goddard Space Flight Center

Appendix 2
Solar Eclipse Schedule

CALENDAR DATE	ECLIPSE TYPE	TIME OF GREATEST ECLIPSE (UTC)	GEOGRAPHIC REGION OF ECLIPSE VISIBILITY
July 2, 2019	Total	19:24	**Total:** central Argentina and Chile, Tuamotu Archipelago. **Partial:** South America, Easter Island, Galapagos Islands, Southern Central America, Polynesia.
December 26, 2019	Annular	5:18:53	**Annular:** northeastern Saudi Arabia, Bahrain, Qatar, United Arab Emirates, Oman, Lakshadweep, Southern India, Sri Lanka, Northern Sumatra, southern Malaysia, Singapore, Borneo, central Indonesia, Palau, Micronesia, Guam. **Partial:** Asia, western Melanesia, northwestern Australia, Middle East, East Africa.
June 21, 2020	Annular	6:41:15	**Annular:** Democratic Republic of the Congo, Sudan, Ethiopia, Eritrea, Yemen, Empty Quarter, Oman, southern Pakistan, northern India, New Delhi, Tibet, southern China, Chongqing, Taiwan. **Partial:** Asia, southeastern Europe, Africa, Middle East, West Melanesia, western Australia, Northern Territory, Cape York Peninsula.
December 14, 2020	Total	16:15	**Total:** southern Chile and Argentina, Kiribati, Polynesia. **Partial:** central and southern South America, southwestern Africa, Antarctic Peninsula, Ellsworth Land, western Queen Maud Land.
June 10, 2021	Annular	10:43	**Annular:** northern Canada, Greenland, Russia. **Partial:** northern North America, Europe, Asia.
December 4, 2021	Total	7:35	**Total:** Antarctica. **Partial:** South Africa, South Atlantic.
April 30, 2022	Partial	20:43	**Partial:** southeast Pacific, southern South America.
October 25, 2022	Partial	11:01	**Partial:** Europe, northeastern Africa, Middle East, western Asia.
April 20, 2023	Hybrid	4:18	**Hybrid:** Indonesia, Australia, Papua New Guinea. **Partial:** southeastern Asia, East Indies, Philippines, New Zealand.
October 14, 2023	Annular	18:01	**Annular:** western United States, Central America, Colombia, Brazil. **Partial:** North America, Central America, South America.
April 8, 2024	Total	18:18	**Total:** Mexico, central United States, eastern Canada. **Partial:** North America, Central America.
October 2, 2024	Annular	18:46	**Annular:** southern Chile, southern Argentina. **Partial:** Pacific, southern South America.
March 29, 2025	Partial	10:49	**Partial:** northwestern Africa, Europe, northern Russia.
September 21, 2025	Partial	19:43	**Partial:** South Pacific, New Zealand, Antarctica.
February 17, 2026	Annular	12:13	**Annular:** Antarctica. **Partial:** southern Argentina, Chile, South Africa, Antarctica.
August 12, 2026	Total	17:47	**Total:** Arctic, Greenland, Iceland, Spain, northeastern Portugal. **Partial:** northern North America, Western Africa, Europe.
February 6, 2027	Annular	16:01	**Annular:** Chile, Argentina, Atlantic. **Partial:** South America, Antarctica, western and southern Africa
August 2, 2027	Total	10:08	**Total:** Morocco, Spain, Algeria, Libya, Egypt, Saudi Arabia, Yemen, Somalia. **Partial:** Africa, Europe, Middle East, West and South Asia.
January 26, 2028	Annular	15:09	**Annular:** Ecuador, Peru, Brazil, Suriname, Spain, Portugal. **Partial:** eastern North America, Central and South America, western Europe, northwestern Africa.
July 22, 2028	Total	2:57	**Total:** Australia, New Zealand. **Partial:** Southeast Asia, East Indies.
January 14, 2029	Partial	17:14	**Partial:** North America, Central America.
June 12, 2029	Partial	4:06	**Partial:** Arctic, Scandinavia, Alaska, northern Asia, northern Canada.
July 11, 2029	Partial	15:37	**Partial:** southern Chile, southern Argentina.
December 5, 2029	Partial	15:04	**Partial:** southern Argentina, southern Chile, Antarctica.
June 1, 2030	Annular	6:29	**Annular:** Algeria, Tunisia, Greece, Turkey, Russia, northern China, Japan. **Partial:** Europe, northern Africa, Mid East, Asia, Arctic, Alaska.

Glossary

ANNULAR ECLIPSE — A solar eclipse where the Moon perfectly aligns with the Sun, but is so distant from Earth that it is too small to block all of the Sun's disk. **Safe viewing of an annular eclipse requires the use of proper eclipse viewers.**

ALBEDO — A measure of how reflective a surface is. Different lunar terrains are often characterized by their reflectivity or albedo.

APOGEE — The point where a satellite (including the Moon) is farthest from Earth in its orbit. (See also perigee.)

BRECCIA — A type of rock formed by the smashing, melting, and remixing of rock caused by a meteoroid impact.

CELESTIAL SPHERE — Imaginary dome, centred on the observer, upon which we map the position of the stars in the sky.

EARTHSHINE — Sunlight reflected off the Earth that dimly illuminates the nighttime side of the Moon.

ECLIPTIC — An imaginary line in the celestial sphere that the Sun appears to travel along during the course of a year.

FAR SIDE — The side of the Moon that is not visible from Earth (often mislabelled the Dark Side).

FAULT (LUNAR) — Often called by its Latin name, *Rupes*, this is a break in the surface of the Moon caused by asteroid impacts or ancient volcanic activity.

LIBRATION — The apparent east–west and north–south rocking of the lunar sphere, caused primarily by the eccentricity and inclination of the Moon's orbit. A favourable libration makes it easier to view features near the illuminated limb.

LIMB — The edge of the Moon as seen from the observer's location, where the Moon meets the sky. Except during the Full Moon, a portion of the limb may be illuminated while the rest is dark.

LUNAR DAY — A period of 29 (Earth) days, 12 hours, and 44 minutes — the time from one sunrise (or sunset) to the next at a fixed location on the Moon.

LUNAR ECLIPSE — When the Moon is aligned with the Earth's shadow cast by the Sun, so that all or part of the Moon receives no direct sunlight. The Moon may appear to turn red.

LUNAR OCCULTATION AND GRAZING OCCULTATION — When the Moon passes in front of a planet or star, and when the lunar limb grazes a planet or star.

MARE — Pronounced *mah-ray*, this Latin term means "sea" and refers to the dark planes on the lunar surface. The plural is *maria* (pronounced *mah-ree-ah*).

MOONRISE AND MOONSET — The exact time the Moon rises or sets relative to your local horizon.

NEAR SIDE — The side of the Moon visible to observers on Earth.

ORBIT — The curved (primarily elliptical) path an object, such as the Moon, travels around a larger object, such as the Earth.

PENUMBRA — During a lunar eclipse, this refers to the outermost part of the Earth's shadow, where sunlight is only partially blocked.

PERIGEE — The point where a satellite (including the Moon) is closest to Earth in its orbit. (See also apogee.)

PHASES — The changing appearance of the Moon during its orbit caused by sunlight striking its surface from different angles.

RAYS — Bright deposits that occur in a radial pattern around recently formed (within the last 100 million years) lunar craters.

RILLE — A depression or groove in the Moon's surface. Often called by the Latin name, *rima* or *rimae* (plural).

SELENOGRAPHY — The practice of studying the surface features of the Moon especially prior to the invention of powerful telescopes and space probes.

TERMINATOR — The irregular boundary, roughly north–south, between the lunar day and lunar night, where the Sun is rising (waxing Moon) or setting (waning Moon).

TIDES — The rise and fall of Earth's sea level primarily due to the gravitational influence of the Moon.

UMBRA — During a lunar eclipse, this refers to the part of the Earth's shadow where the sunlight is completely (as opposed to partially) blocked.

NON-SCIENTIFIC TERMS YOU MAY HEAR, BUT ARE NOT INCLUDED IN THIS BOOK

BLOOD MOON — Another word for lunar eclipse, rarely used by astronomers, with origins in the Bible.

BLUE MOON — Two Full Moons in one calendar month, which occurs because the Moon's 29.5-day cycle is shorter than all months but February.

DARK SIDE OF THE MOON — An album by the rock band Pink Floyd. The phrase "dark side" is frequently confused with "far side."

SUPERMOON — A Full or New Moon that occurs when the Moon is near perigee in its orbit. A Full Supermoon appears only seven per cent larger than an average Full Moon. Ocean tides at both New and Full Supermoons can be up to 25 per cent higher. The term was introduced by a twentieth-century astrologer and there is no accepted astronomical definition of the term.

Photo Credits

Primary lunar images were originally taken by the author using either his personal twelve-inch Dobsonian telescope, eight-inch Dobsonian telescope, or Saint Mary's University's Burke-Gaffney Observatory (iPhone to eyepiece). Others were made by the author using data from NASA's Scientific Visualization Studio or Stellarium astronomy software. All other image credits provided below:

Celestron: p. 23 (inset)

Chinese Academy of Sciences/NAOC/Science and Application Center for Moon and Deepspace Exploration: p. 56 (inset)

Creative Commons: p. 65 (inset, 1791)

David M. F. Chapman: p. 19 (top)

Dr. Roy Bishop: p. 11 (Ring of Fire)

Hercules Assisting Atlas by Claude Mellan: p. 25

NASA (Images follow NASA's photo usage guidelines): p. 5, p. 22 (top), p. 31, p. 36 (inset images), p. 37, p. 38 (top), p. 39 (top), p. 41 (top), p. 44 (inset), p. 45, p. 55, p. 60 (top), p. 63 (inset), p. 66 (top), p. 67 (top), p. 71 (top), p. 75

NASA/GSFC/Arizona State University: p. 15

Public Domain: p. 4, p. 20 (inset), p. 28 (top), p. 64 (inset), p. 66 (inset), p. 69 (top), p. 71 (inset), p. 73 (top)

Shutterstock: p. 43 (inset)

Tim Doucette: p. 11 (Total Solar Eclipse)

Bibliography and Further Reading

21st Century Atlas of the Moon by Charles A. Wood and Maurice J. S. Collins

Atlas of the Moon by Antonín Rükl

Field Map of the Moon and *Mirror-Image Field Map of the Moon* (*Sky & Telescope*)

"Lunar Observing," *Observer's Handbook* by Royal Astronomical Society of Canada (RASC), published annually

The Modern Moon: A Personal View by Charles A. Wood

The Moon and How to Observe It: An Advanced Handbook for Students of the Moon in the 21st Century by Peter Grego

Miscellaneous non-lunar facts drawn from *Encyclopedia Britannica*

WEBSITES AND SOFTWARE

International Occultation Timing Association: *www.lunar-occultations.com/iota/iotandx.htm*

LRO Quick map: *quickmap.lroc.asu.edu/*

Mi'kmaw Moons project page: *www.facebook.com/www.MikmawMoons*

Moon Atlas (iOS and MacOS)

NASA's Moon Page: *solarsystem.nasa.gov/moons/earths-moon/overview/*

NASA's Lunar Reconnaissance Orbiter: *lunar.gsfc.nasa.gov/*

RASC lunar observing programs with certificates and pins: *www.rasc.ca/observing*

Stellarium: *www.stellarium.org*

Surface Journal of Every Apollo Mission: *www.hq.nasa.gov/alsj/main.html*

WHO TO FOLLOW ON TWITTER

Author: *@JohnAaronRead*

Lunar Reconnaissance Orbiter: *@LRO_NASA*

NASA's Moon page: *@NASAMoon*

Astronomy Nova Scotia: *@astronomyns*

Made in the USA
Coppell, TX
07 February 2023